a companion to
MODAL LOGIC

a companion to
MODAL LOGIC

G.E. HUGHES
M.J. CRESSWELL

METHUEN
LONDON and NEW YORK

First published in 1984 by
Methuen & Co. Ltd
11 New Fetter Lane, London EC4P 4EE

Published in the USA by
Methuen & Co.
in association with Methuen, Inc.
733 Third Avenue, New York, NY 10017

Printed in Great Britain
by Richard Clay (The Chaucer Press), Ltd
Bungay, Suffolk

British Library Cataloguing in Publication Data
Hughes, G.E.
A companion to modal logic.
1. Modality (Logic)
I. Title   II. Cresswell, M.J.
160   BC199.M6

ISBN 0-416-37500-6
ISBN 0-416-37510-3 Pbk

Library of Congress Cataloging in Publication Data
Hughes, G.E. (George Edward), 1918 –
A companion to modal logic.

Bibliography: p.
Includes index.
1. Modality (Logic)   I. Cresswell, M.J.   II. Title.
BX199.M6H795   1984   160   84-8939
ISBN 0-416-37500-6
ISBN 0-416-37510-3 (pbk.)

To
BERYL and MARY

Contents

Preface

An earlier book of ours, entitled *An Introduction to Modal Logic* (*IML*), was published in 1968. When we wrote it, we were able to give a reasonably comprehensive survey of the state of modal logic at that time. We very much doubt, however, whether any comparable survey would be possible today, for, since 1968, the subject has developed vigorously in a wide variety of directions. The present book is therefore not an attempt to update *IML* in the style of that work, but it is in some sense a sequel to it. The bulk of *IML* was concerned with the description of a range of particular modal systems. We have made no attempt here to survey the very large number of systems found in the recent literature. Good surveys of these will be found in Lemmon and Scott (1977), Segerberg (1971) and Chellas (1980), and we have not wished to duplicate the material found in these works. Our aim has been rather to concentrate on certain recent developments which concern questions about general properties of modal systems and which have, we believe, led to a genuine deepening of our understanding of modal logic. Most of the relevant material is, however, at present available only in journal articles, and then often in a form which is accessible only to a fairly experienced worker in the field. We have tried to make these important developments accessible to all students of modal logic, as we believe they should be.

In choosing which systems to deal with we have confined ourselves, as in *IML*, to those which have only one necessity operator. In addition, we have restricted ourselves to those which are called 'normal', in a sense to be explained in chapter 1. This second restriction excludes a number of the systems discussed in *IML*, but enables us to keep our treatment within manageable bounds.

Except in a few instances, we have adhered to the terminology and notation of *IML*. We have, however, tried to make the book self-contained, so that readers with varying backgrounds in modal logic (perhaps even none) will be able to use it, and not merely those who have approached the subject by studying *IML*. We have included a few exercises at the end of each chapter, except the first, in the hope that this will increase the usefulness of the book as a supplementary textbook. These exercises supplement those given in *IML* or in Chellas (1980).

We shall now give an outline of the main topics the book deals with, and indicate how they fit together. In doing so we have in mind readers who already know a little modal logic, and in particular those whose knowledge of the subject comes from *IML*. We hope, however, that what we say will be of assistance to others as well, especially if they consult the glossary from time to time.

Readers of *IML* will no doubt recall that a great deal of that work was concerned with the connection between a system of modal logic, specified as a class of formulae derived from certain axioms by certain transformation rules, and a class of structures called *models*. For normal propositional modal logic a model (both in *IML* and as defined in chapter 1 of the present book) is a triple ⟨ W, R, V ⟩, in which W is a non-empty set whose members we call 'worlds', R is a dyadic relation defined over W, and V is a value-assignment of the kind described on pp. 7f. We say that a formula is valid in a certain model if it is true in every world in it.

Typically, what we do in *IML* is first to present a modal system, then to introduce a class of models (as it might be, the class of all models in which R is reflexive), and finally, in one way or another, to show, or at least indicate, that the system is *characterized* by the class of models in question, in the sense that a formula is a theorem of the system if and only if it is valid in every model in that class. A characterization proof has two stages: first we show that the system is *sound* with respect to the class of models, i.e. that every theorem is valid in every model in the class; and secondly we show that the system is *complete* with respect to the class, i.e. that every formula which is valid in every model in the class is a theorem.

One of the first results obtained in the present book (in chapter 2) consists in showing, by a completely general method, that *every* normal modal system is characterized by some class of models, and indeed that every such system is characterized by a single model known as its *canonical model*. Using the general theory of canonical models, we can then readily prove that each of the 'landmark' systems, T, S4, B and S5, as well as a number of others, is characterized by a class of models in which R satisfies a certain specifiable condition. In chapter 3 we study ways of establishing, at one blow, the characterization of a large range of modal systems by 'translating' their axioms into formulae of the lower predicate calculus which define the classes of models which characterize the systems in question.

Specifying a class of models by a condition on R is of course a way of specifying it without any reference to a value-assignment; and it is plausible to suggest that we ought to define the validity of a formula without any such reference, since validity in logic is often thought of as implying truth for *every* value-assignment to the variables of the relevant language. To achieve such a definition of validity, we introduce in chapter 4 the notion of a *frame*, which is simply the ⟨ W, R ⟩ part of a model. We then say that a formula is valid on a certain frame if it is valid in *every* model based on that frame, no matter what value-assignment it may contain, and that a system is characterized by a certain class of frames if its theorems are precisely the formulae that are valid on every frame in that class.

A consideration of frames leads to what is perhaps the most surprising result in the whole book. Although the canonical model method described in chapter 2 shows that every normal modal system is characterized by a class of *models*, we produce in chapter 4 a normal modal system of which we prove that it is not characterized by any class of *frames* at all. Such a system we call, in an absolute sense of the term, *incomplete*.

The distinction between frames and models opens up a whole new series of questions. For example, the system T is known to be characterized by the class of all reflexive models, and therefore by the class of all reflexive frames. In chapter 6, however, we show that *all* the frames for T are reflexive, though not all the models for T are; and analogous results obtain for S4, B, S5 and many other systems. We can also ask what the frames of canonical models look like; and in this same chapter we are able to show that some of them contain worlds which are related to every world in the frame, while others split into a number of completely disconnected parts. There even turn out to be systems in which some of the theorems are not valid on the frame of the relevant canonical model. This again may appear to be a surprising fact, in view of the result obtained in chapter 2 that all the theorems of any system are valid in the canonical model for that system; but we have to remember that a formula might be valid in a certain model and yet not valid in some other model based on the same frame. Some of the results reached in chapter 6 are proved by methods introduced in the preceding chapter, which is mainly devoted to a study of methods whereby we can pass from validity on one frame to validity on another.

In chapter 7 we extend a method of proving completeness which is used in *IML*, to give a number of new results, including some to the effect that various systems are characterized by classes of frames with a 'tree' structure, or even by single frames distinct from the frames of their canonical models. In chapter 8 we take up the question of whether a system can be characterized by a class of models each of which is finite, and we find that some systems can be so characterized but that others cannot.

Finally, although this book is mainly about propositional modal logic, we have included a chapter on modal predicate logic in which we consider how far, and in what ways, some of the properties of modal propositional systems carry over to their predicate logic counterparts.

The Wellington logic seminar bore the brunt of earlier versions of most of what is in this book; Rob Goldblatt in particular gave us valuable help. We are grateful also for much encouragement from Krister Segerberg. Kit Fine read the whole manuscript before its final revision, and made many suggestions which led, we believe, to its substantial improvement. Finally, with great skill and a willingness which went far beyond the call of duty, Helen Fleming turned our handwriting into a clear and orderly typescript.

Wellington   G.E.H.
New Zealand   M.J.C.
June 1984

Note on references

The only work mentioned by name in the text itself is the present authors' *An Introduction to Modal Logic* (1968), which is referred to as '*IML*' throughout. All other references are given in the notes, by surname of author and date of publication. Full details will be found in the bibliography on pp. 186–8. For the sake of brevity, when a result has been mentioned or a work cited in *IML*, we usually give the *IML* reference only. It should be emphasized that this is not in any way intended as a claim that the result in question is our own. Bibliographical details will in these cases be found in *IML* itself.

A special comment is needed about the work by Lemmon and Scott (*The 'Lemmon Notes'*) to which we refer frequently. This unfinished but very influential work was written shortly before Lemmon's death in 1966, and began to be circulated privately among modal logicians, in mimeographed form, at about the time when *IML* was going through the press. It did not, however, appear in print until 1977. We therefore refer to it as 'Lemmon and Scott (1977)', but in discussing it we treat it as if it had been published several years before that.

1 Normal propositional modal systems

This first chapter has two main aims. One is to give a general account of the propositional modal systems that we shall be dealing with in this book, with some examples of the most important of them. The other is to explain the notion of validity as it applies to formulae of modal logic.

The propositional calculus

We first set out a version of the classical propositional calculus, which we call *PC*.

The language of PC takes as primitive or undefined symbols the following:

1. A denumerably infinite set of *sentence letters*, which we write as $p, q, r, \ldots$, with or without numerical subscripts;

2. The four symbols $\sim$, $\vee$, (and).

Certain sequences of these symbols count as *well-formed formulae* (*wff*) of PC. The sequences in question are all and only those which are constructed in accordance with the following *formation rules*:

FR1 Any sentence letter is a wff.

FR2 If α is a wff, so is $\sim \alpha$.

FR3 If α and β are wff, so is $(\alpha \vee \beta)$.

We usually omit (and) when they enclose a complete wff, but not when they enclose any proper part of one.

We interpret the sentence letters as variables whose values are propositions. For this reason we shall henceforth refer to them as 'propositional variables', or simply as 'variables'. We assume that each proposition is either true or false, but not both. Truth and falsity are said to be *truth-values*; thus every proposition has exactly one truth-value. We shall use '1' for the truth-value *true* and '0' for the truth-value *false*.

We interpret $\sim$ and $\vee$ as follows: For any proposition p, if p is true then $\sim p$ is false, and if p is false then $\sim p$ is true. And for any propositions p and q, $(p \vee q)$ is true if at least one of p and q is true, and false if both p and q are false.

This can be expressed more exactly by using the notion of a *PC value-assignment*. The basic idea here is that we assign truth-values to the variables in a wff, and then use the principles we have just stated to work out the resulting truth-value of the whole wff. In more precise terms, V is a PC value-assignment if and only if (iff) it satisfies the following conditions:

1. For any variable p, either $V(p) = 1$ or $V(p) = 0$, but not both.

2. $[V \sim]$ For any wff α, $V(\sim \alpha) = 1$ if $V(\alpha) = 0$; otherwise $V(\sim \alpha) = 0$.

3. $[V \vee]$ For any wff α and β, $V(\alpha \vee \beta) = 1$ if $V(\alpha) = 1$ or $V(\beta) = 1$; otherwise $V(\alpha \vee \beta) = 0$.

A wff which has the value 1 for all PC value-assignments is said to be *PC-valid* or to be a *PC-tautology*.

$\sim$ and $\vee$ are called *operators*. Other operators can be defined in terms of them, and we introduce three by the following definitions, where α and β are any wff:

$[\text{Def.}]$ $\quad (\alpha . \beta) \ =_{\text{Df}} \sim (\sim \alpha \vee \sim \beta)$

$[\text{Def} \supset]$ $\quad (\alpha \supset \beta) =_{\text{Df}} (\sim \alpha \vee \beta)$

$[\text{Def} \equiv]$ $\quad (\alpha \equiv \beta) =_{\text{Df}} ((\alpha \supset \beta).(\beta \supset \alpha))$

We can conveniently read $\sim \alpha$ as 'not α', $\alpha \vee \beta$ as 'α or β', $\alpha . \beta$ as 'α and β', $\alpha \supset \beta$ as 'if α, β', and $\alpha \equiv \beta$ as 'α if and only if β'. The interpretations of ., $\supset$ and $\equiv$ are of course fixed by their definitions together with the interpretations already given to $\sim$ and $\vee$. They are expressed in the following consequential conditions on PC value-assignments:

[V.] $V(\alpha . \beta) = 1$ if both $V(\alpha) = 1$ and $V(\beta) = 1$; otherwise $V(\alpha . \beta) = 0$.

[V ⊃] $V(\alpha \supset \beta) = 1$ if either $V(\alpha) = 0$ or $V(\beta) = 1$; otherwise $V(\alpha \supset \beta) = 0$.

[V ≡] $V(\alpha \equiv \beta) = 1$ if $V(\alpha) = V(\beta)$; otherwise $V(\alpha \equiv \beta) = 0$.

Various other versions of the classical propositional calculus can be devised by taking some other combinations of symbols as primitive. For the issues discussed in this book, however, nothing turns on which version we adopt, so long as all the operators we have mentioned occur either as primitive or as defined.

Modal propositional logic
The operators mentioned so far are all of the kind known as *truth-functional*. What this means is that whenever a proposition is formed by them out of one or more simpler propositions, its truth-value depends only on the truth-values of those simpler propositions. In modal logic, however, we have in addition a pair of operators (*modal* operators) which are not intended to be truth-functional, and which we shall write as L and M. We take L as primitive and define M. The new formation rule is

   FR4   If α is a wff, so is $L\alpha$

and the definition is

   [Def M] $M\alpha =_{\mathrm{Df}} \sim L \sim \alpha$

(Note that many writers use the symbols $\Box$ and $\Diamond$ as we use L and M respectively.)

   L and M can be given a variety of interpretations, though of course if we settle on a certain interpretation of L, a corresponding interpretation of M will be forced on us by its definition. Modal logic was originally developed as a logic of necessity and possibility, and L and M are often read as 'necessarily' and 'possibly' respectively. If, however, we want to use such notions as an intuitive guide to understanding modal formulae, we should be prepared to think of them in a liberal and flexible way. When we say that something is necessary, we may mean that it is logically necessary, or that it is 'deontically' necessary (i.e.

required for the fulfilling of an obligation), or that it is unpreventable, or that it will be true ever hereafter, or that it is prescribed by the rules of a certain game, or any one of a number of other things. Such concepts differ importantly among themselves; if we have logical necessity in mind, for example, we shall presumably want to maintain that whatever is necessary is true, but if we are thinking about deontic necessity we are unlikely to want to say this, since it would commit us to saying that everything that ought to be the case is the case. Our use of L is not intended to tie us to any one of these interpretations in particular;[1] in fact, in this book we shall hardly ever be concerned with intuitive interpretations of this kind, let alone with questions about their philosophical analysis. The sorts of interpretations we shall be interested in are ones which generalize the notion of a value-assignment which we have already defined for PC. We shall explain what these interpretations are a little later on in this chapter.

Normal modal systems
By a *system of modal logic* we shall, in this book, mean simply a certain kind of class of formulae of the language of modal logic. Where S is such a class of formulae, we shall call its members its *theorems*, and we shall write '$\vdash_S \alpha$' to mean that α is a theorem of S. When there is no confusion about which system is involved we shall usually simply write '$\vdash \alpha$'. The class of all wff is known as the *inconsistent* system. All other systems are said to be *consistent*.

In this book we shall confine our attention to those modal systems which are known as *normal* ones.[2] A system S of modal logic is said to be normal if it can be specified in the following way:

First, S contains as theorems all PC-valid wff.

Secondly, S contains the following formula

K $L(p \supset q) \supset (Lp \supset Lq)$

Thirdly, S satisfies a number of principles to the effect that if certain wff are theorems of S, then so are certain other wff which are related to them in certain ways. Such principles are often called *transformation rules*, and there are three such rules which any normal modal system must satisfy. To simplify the statement of these, we introduce some new notation and terminology. We shall write '$\vdash \alpha \rightarrow \vdash \beta$' to mean that if α is a theorem (of S), so is β. We also define a *substitution-instance* of a wff α as any wff which is obtained from α by replacing the variables $p_1, \ldots, p_n$, wherever they occur in α, by any wff $\beta_1, \ldots, \beta_n$ respectively.

Using this notation and terminology, we state the transformation rules of any normal modal system as follows:

US (uniform substitution): If α is a theorem, so is every substitution-instance of α.

MP (modus ponens): $\vdash \alpha$ and $\vdash \alpha \supset \beta \rightarrow \vdash \beta$.

N (necessitation): $\vdash \alpha \rightarrow \vdash L\alpha$.

We note at this point that all the theorems and rules of the system T which are given on pp. 30–40 of *IML*, with the exception of A5 and T1, are theorems and rules of every normal modal system. We mention a few of these because of their importance for later developments, giving them, for the sake of uniformity, the same names as in *IML*:

The law of *L-distribution* (T3 in *IML*):

$$L(p.q) \equiv (Lp.Lq)$$

DR1: $\vdash \alpha \supset \beta \rightarrow \vdash L\alpha \supset L\beta$

DR3: $\vdash \alpha \supset \beta \rightarrow \vdash M\alpha \supset M\beta$

Eq   (substitution of equivalents): If $\vdash \alpha \equiv \beta$, and if γ and δ differ only in that γ may have α in one or more places where δ has β, then $\vdash \gamma \equiv \delta$ (and hence if $\vdash \gamma$ then $\vdash \delta$).

LMI (*L-M* interchange): If α is any wff which contains an unbroken sequence of *L*s and/or *M*s, and β results from α by replacing *L* by *M* and *M* by *L* throughout that sequence and also inserting or deleting a $\sim$ both immediately before and immediately after that sequence, then $\vdash \alpha \equiv \beta$ (and hence if $\vdash \alpha$ then $\vdash \beta$).

One common way of presenting a particular normal modal system is by stipulating that it contains, in addition to the PC-tautologies, a certain specified collection of other formulae. These formulae, which must contain **K** but otherwise can be any collection we choose, are then said to be *axioms* of the system; and in that case its theorems are precisely those wff which can be derived from its axioms and the PC-valid wff by means of the transformation rules US, MP and N. When a system is presented in this way, we are said to have provided an *axiomatic basis* for it, or to have *axiomatized* it.[3] In general, one and the same system can be axiomatized in many different ways; that is to say, there are many different collections of wff, each of which, if added to the elements that are common to all normal modal systems, would yield precisely the same wff as theorems.

If a system is specified in some non-axiomatic way, the question then arises of how it can be axiomatized; and as we have just noted, there may be a variety of answers to this question. A more general question of considerable interest is whether there are normal modal systems which cannot be axiomatized at all. We have to be careful, however, how we formulate this question. In the widest sense, to say that a normal modal system S is axiomatizable is simply to say that there is a set A of wff (axioms) such that the members of S are precisely those wff that can be derived from the members of A by US, MP and N. But such an account of axiomatizability is too wide to be useful; for it would allow us to take all the wff in S as our axioms and count this as an axiomatization of S, so that it would, in this sense, be trivially true that every system is axiomatizable. What is usually meant, however, by saying that S is axiomatizable is that there is an *effectively specifiable* set of wff whose consequences are precisely the members of S. And in this sense there are normal modal systems which can be shown not to be axiomatizable at all.[4]

If a normal modal system S is axiomatizable in the sense we have just described, the question arises whether it is *finitely* axiomatizable, i.e. whether there is some *finite* set of wff which, together with the PC-tautologies, yield by US, MP and N precisely the wff in S. All the systems we shall specifically mention by name in this book are in fact finitely axiomatizable, but there are some quite simple normal modal systems which, though axiomatizable, are not finitely axiomatizable.[5]

The weakest normal modal system is called K, and its theorems are precisely those wff which are theorems of every normal system.[6] K can be axiomatized by adding to the PC-valid wff the single formula **K** mentioned above, viz. $L(p \supset q) \supset (Lp \supset Lq)$. In fact that formula and the system are given the same name for that reason.

Models

An important way of studying normal propositional modal systems is provided by the use of *models*. A model, in this context, is a triple $\langle$ W, R, V $\rangle$, where W is a non-empty set, R is a dyadic relation defined over the members of W, and V is a value-assignment of a kind to be described in a moment. W can be any non-empty set we please of any kind of things whatsoever, and for this reason its members are sometimes referred to by the non-committal term 'points'. They are also, however, sometimes called 'worlds', or 'possible worlds', because one of the intuitive ideas underlying the model-theory is that a proposition is necessary iff it is true in all possible worlds; and this is the terminology we shall use in this book. Since we wish to speak of a proposition's being true or false in a given possible world, we cannot proceed, as we did in the case of PC, by letting V assign a truth-value to a variable *simpliciter*; rather, we must think of a truth-value as assigned to a variable with respect to, or in, or at a given possible world. Thus our rule for V is that for every variable p and every $w \in$ W,

Either $V(p, w) = 1$ or $V(p, w) = 0$, but not both.

Finally, R is simply a set of ordered pairs of worlds in W; and where w and w' are in W, we say that wRw' iff the pair $\langle w, w' \rangle$ is in the set R. R is often called the *accessibility* relation, and when wRw' we say, interchangeably, that w is *related to* w', or that w' is *accessible from* w, or, more picturesquely, that w *can see* w'.

In summary, a model $\langle$ W, R, V $\rangle$ is unambiguously and completely determined by (a) what the members of W are, (b) for which pairs of members of W, w and w', wRw' holds and (c) in which members of W which variables are assigned 1 and which are assigned 0.

We now state rules which show how, given a model $\langle$ W, R, V $\rangle$, the truth-value of any wff in any world in W is uniquely determined:

[V $\sim$]   For any wff α and any $w \in$ W, $V(\sim \alpha, w) = 1$ if $V(\alpha, w) = 0$; otherwise $V(\sim \alpha, w) = 0$.

[V $\vee$]   For any wff α and β and any $w \in$ W, $V(\alpha \vee \beta, w) = 1$ if either $V(\alpha, w) = 1$ or $V(\beta, w) = 1$; otherwise $V(\alpha \vee \beta, w) = 0$.

[VL]   For any wff α and any $w \in W$, $V(L\alpha, w) = 1$ if $V(\alpha, w') = 1$ for every $w' \in W$ such that wRw'; otherwise $V(L\alpha, w) = 0$.

[V $\sim$] and [V $\vee$] are of course simply the PC rules for $\sim$ and $\vee$, generalized to apply to each world in a model. [VL] expresses the idea that $L\alpha$ is true in a world iff α itself is true in every world accessible from that world.

The rules for ., $\supset$ and $\equiv$ are easily derived from [V $\sim$] and [V $\vee$] as in the case of PC. [VL], together with the definition of M as $\sim L \sim$, gives us the following rule for M:

[VM]   For any wff α and any $w \in W$, $V(M\alpha, w) = 1$ if there is some $w' \in W$ such that wRw' and $V(\alpha, w') = 1$; otherwise $V(M\alpha, w) = 0$.

In other words, $M\alpha$ is true in a world iff α is true in *some* world accessible from that world.

It is a straightforward matter to derive from [VL] and [VM] generalized forms of these rules. To state these, we introduce two pieces of notation, which we shall employ frequently later on:

First, we shall write 'L^n' for a sequence of n consecutive Ls, and 'M^n' for a sequence of n consecutive Ms. Thus $L^4 p$ is $LLLLp$, $M^2 L^3 p$ is $MMLLLp$, $L^0 p$ is simply p, and so on.

Secondly, we shall write '$wR^n w'$' to mean that w is related to w' in n R-steps, in the sense that $wR^2 w'$ iff there is a $w*$ such that $wRw*$ and $w*Rw'$, and that in general, $wR^n w'$ iff there are $w_1, \ldots, w_{n-1}$ such that wRw_1 and ... and $w_{n-1} Rw'$. We interpret $wR^0 w'$ to mean that $w = w'$.

Given this notation, we can state the generalized forms of [VL] and [VM] as follows:

[VL*]   For any wff α and any $w \in W$, $V(L^n\alpha, w) = 1$ if $V(\alpha, w') = 1$ for every $w' \in W$ such that $wR^n w'$; otherwise $V(L^n \alpha, w) = 0$.

[VM*]   For any wff α and any $w \in W$, $V(M^n\alpha, w) = 1$ if there is some $w' \in W$ such that $wR^n w'$ and $V(\alpha, w') = 1$; otherwise $V(M^n \alpha, w) = 0$.

We leave it to the reader to derive these rules from the original [VL] and [VM].

Note that nothing we have said rules out the possibility that a model might contain worlds which are not related (by **R**) to any worlds at all, even to themselves. Segerberg has called such worlds *dead ends*.[7] The question arises of how we are to evaluate wff of the forms $L\alpha$ and $M\alpha$ in a dead end. And the answer that $[VL]$ and $[VM]$ give us is that if w is a dead end, then $V(L\alpha, w) = 1$ and $V(M\alpha, w) = 0$, no matter what wff α may be. $[VM]$ is perhaps the clearer case of the two, since if w is a dead end there is no $w' \in W$ such that $w\mathbf{R}w'$. But if we understand $[VL]$ correctly, the result is clear there too: for we intend '$V(\alpha, w') = 1$ for every w' such that $w\mathbf{R}w''$ to mean 'there is no w' such that both $w\mathbf{R}w'$ and $V(\alpha, w') \neq 1$' and if there is no w' at all such that $w\mathbf{R}w'$, then this condition is automatically, if trivially, satisfied. We shall have a good deal to say about dead ends in later chapters.[8]

It is also worth noting that, given a model $\langle W, R, V \rangle$, many authors use the notation $\langle W, R, V \rangle \vDash _w\alpha$ instead of our $V(\alpha, w) = 1$, and $\langle W, R, V \rangle \nvDash _w\alpha$ or $\langle W, R, V \rangle \dashv _w\alpha$ instead of our $V(\alpha, w) = 0$.

Validity

Our account of models leads up to a definition of validity which is applicable to wff of propositional modal logic – in fact, as we shall see, to a whole series of such definitions. As a first step, we define *validity in a model* by saying that a wff α is valid in the model $\langle W, R, V \rangle$ iff $V(\alpha, w) = 1$ for every $w \in W$. The kind of validity in which we are chiefly interested, however, is not validity in a single model but validity in every model in a certain class. The general theme that will run through our various definitions of validity, in fact, is that validity is truth in every world in every model of a certain specified kind.

The first class of models we shall consider is simply the class of all models.

THEOREM 1.1
Every theorem of K is valid in every model.

PROOF
The proof proceeds by showing (1) that every axiom of K is valid in every model and (2) that the transformation rules are validity-preserving for the class of models in question (i.e. the

class of all models), in the sense that if they are applied to any wff which are valid in all models, the resulting wff must also be valid in all models.

For (1), consider any world w in any model $\langle$ W, R, V $\rangle$. Now V gives a PC value-assignment to the variables at w; so any PC-tautology must be true at w. To show that **K** is true at w it is sufficient to show that if $L(p \supset q)$ and Lp are both true in w, so is Lq. Now if $L(p \supset q)$ and Lp are true in w, then by [VL], $p \supset q$ and p are true in every world accessible from w. Hence by [V $\supset$], so is q; so by [VL] again, Lq is true at w.

For (2): If α is valid in every model, then α is true in every world w irrespective of what truth-values the variables have in w. Hence if β results from α by uniform replacement of the variables in α by any wff, then since each of these wff must have some truth-value in w, β too must be true in w. So US preserves validity. MP also preserves validity, since if α and $\alpha \supset \beta$ are true in every world in every model, [V $\supset$] shows that the same holds for β. Finally, if α is true in every world in every model, then *a fortiori* it is true in every world accessible from any world; hence $L\alpha$ is also true in every world, and so N preserves validity.

This completes the proof.

In the next chapter we shall prove the converse of Theorem 1.1, that every wff which is valid in every model is a theorem of **K**.

Some extensions of K

K, as we have said, is the weakest normal modal system. The simplest way of obtaining extensions of **K** is by adding extra axioms, and we shall now briefly present four systems that are obtainable in this way. These are the systems studied in Part I of *IML*, viz. T, S4, B (the Brouwerian system) and S5.

The system T is **K** with the additional axiom

T $\quad Lp \supset p$

S4 is T with the further addition of the axiom

4 $\quad Lp \supset LLp$

B is T with the addition of

B $\quad \sim p \supset L \sim Lp$

and S5 is T with

E $\sim Lp \supset L \sim Lp$[9]

These systems are related to one another and to K in the way indicated in the following diagram:

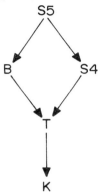

Here the notation 'S → S'' means that S properly contains S', i.e. that the theorems of S include all the theorems of S' and others as well.

These five systems are only a small sample of the many that are known. Even with our present material we can easily form others by adding **4**, **B** or **E** directly to K instead of to T. These systems we call K4, KB and KE respectively. In later chapters we shall introduce a number of other systems, and when we do so we shall either give them names, as we have done for the ones we have so far mentioned, or else use the notation 'S + α' to denote the system formed from the system S by the addition of the wff α as an axiom. However, in this book we shall be concerned with particular systems only in so far as they illustrate certain general principles or techniques. Information about a wider range of systems than we consider here will be found in *IML* and in several other easily accessible works.[10]

Normal modal systems can be studied semantically by restricting in various ways the classes of models to be considered. For the four systems just mentioned, the relevant restrictions consist in imposing certain conditions on the accessibility relation R.

Consider first the condition that R be reflexive. Consider, that is, not the class of all models without exception, but the class of all models in which every world, whatever else it may or may not be related to, is at least related to itself. We shall call such models, for short, *reflexive models*. It is not hard to see that the axiom T is valid in every reflexive model; for if Lp is true in any world w, then if w is related to itself, p must also be true in w. Moreover, our three transformation rules preserve the property of being valid in every such model, as the argument given in the proof of Theorem 1.1 should make clear. This means that every theorem of T is valid in every reflexive model.

We can obtain analogous results for S4, B and S5. The relevant classes of models are: for S4, those which are both reflexive and transitive (i.e. for any w_1, w_2 and $w_3 \in W$, if $w_1 R w_2$ and $w_2 R w_3$ then $w_1 R w_3$); for B, those which are both reflexive and symmetrical (i.e. for any w_1 and $w_2 \in W$, if $w_1 R w_2$ then $w_2 R w_1$); and for S5, those in which R is an equivalence relation (i.e. reflexive, transitive and symmetrical). We omit the details of the proofs, but in each case it is a straightforward matter to show that the axioms of the system are valid in all models in the corresponding class, and simple adaptations of the proof we gave for K will show that the transformation rules preserve validity for the more restricted classes of models under consideration.[11]

When all the theorems of a modal system are valid in all the models in a given class, we say that the system is *sound* with respect to that class. When the converse holds – i.e. when all the wff that are valid in all the models in the class in question are theorems of the system – we say that the system is *complete* with respect to that class. When a system is both sound and complete with respect to a certain class of models, we say that that class of models *characterizes* (or *determines*) the system. So the results we have noted above are to the effect that K, T, S4, B and S5 are all sound with respect to certain classes of models. In the next chapter we shall prove that they are also complete with respect to those same classes of models, and hence that they are characterized by them.

Validity-preservingness in a model

We have seen that the rules US, MP and N are validity-preserving when by 'validity' we mean validity in all models, or in all models in certain classes. But can we say the same if by 'validity' we mean validity in a single model? In other words, is it the case that if a number of wff are all valid in a certain model, then every wff that we can derive from them by US, MP and N will also be valid in that model? In particular, can we be sure that if all the axioms of a given normal modal system are valid in a model $\langle$ W, R, V $\rangle$, then so are all its theorems?

The answer is that we cannot. It is, indeed, easy to show that MP and N are validity-preserving in a single model. For if both α and $\alpha \supset \beta$ are true in every world in W, then by [V $\supset$] so is β. And if α is true in every world in W, then *a fortiori* it is true in every world that any world in W can see; so $L\alpha$ will also be true in every world in W. The same, however, does not hold for US. For to say that US is validity-preserving in a single model would be to say that if a wff α is true in every world in a model, then so is every substitution-instance of α; and it is easy to see that this does not hold generally. To take the simplest case, it is a straightforward matter to define a model in which p is true in every world but q is not; yet q is certainly a substitution-instance of p. Of course, p is not an axiom of any normal modal system (at least not of any consistent one), but the same situation obtains even for a wff that is such an axiom. There is no difficulty, for instance, in defining a model in which $Lp \supset p$ is true in every world but $Lq \supset q$ is not. An example would be a model consisting of only two worlds, w_1 and w_2, where we have $w_1 R w_2$ but neither world is related to itself, and in which p is true in both worlds and q is false in w_1 and true in w_2.

So we cannot be sure that if a collection of wff $\alpha_1, \ldots, \alpha_n$ are all valid in a given model, all the wff derived from them by US, MP and N are also valid in that model. What we *can* be sure of, however, is that these derived wff will be valid in the model if not only $\alpha_1, \ldots, \alpha_n$ themselves but all their substitution-instances are valid in it. As applied to an axiomatically presented normal modal system, this result amounts to this:

THEOREM 1.2
Suppose that S is any axiomatically presented normal modal system, that $\langle W, R, V \rangle$ is any model, and that every substitution-instance of every axiom of S is valid in $\langle W, R, V \rangle$. Then every theorem of S is valid in $\langle W, R, V \rangle$.

We outline how this theorem can be proved, but leave the details to the reader. Suppose we have a model $\langle W, R, V \rangle$. Let us say that a wff is *generalizable* iff all its substitution-instances are valid in $\langle W, R, V \rangle$. Then the hypothesis of the theorem is that all the axioms of S are generalizable. The proof then takes the form of showing that any wff that is obtained from generalizable wff by any of the transformation rules (including US) is itself generalizable.

Theorem 1.2 will be of use to us in later chapters.

Notes

1 On p.22 of *IML* we said that by 'necessity' we meant 'what is often called *logical* necessity'. That perhaps indicated a narrower approach to modal logic than we should now be inclined to adopt; but it was said in a context in which we were asking which principles would be intuitively plausible, given this particular notion of necessity. And even in *IML* we discussed briefly some other interpretations, e.g. on pp. 257 and 302.

2 The main source for this use of the word 'normal' is in Lemmon and Scott (1977). These authors, however, (p. 30) trace its use back to the much earlier work of McKinsey and Tarski.

3 Some authors, e.g. Segerberg (1971), use the word 'logic' for what we are calling a *system of logic*, and reserve the word 'system' for an axiomatic basis, i.e. for a set of axioms and transformation rules. Instead of saying that one and the same system can be axiomatized in many different ways, these authors would say that one and the same logic can be specified by many different systems.

4 For example, the system presented in Urquhart (1981) can be adapted so that its axioms correspond to an arbitrary non-recursively enumerable set of numbers, and the resulting system will not be axiomatizable in the sense referred to.

5 See, e.g., van Benthem (1980), p. 138, and Hughes and Cresswell (1975), p. 21. Some authors (e.g. Segerberg (1971), p. 34) call a logic 'finitely axiomatizable' only if it can be axiomatized by a finite set of axioms with US and MP as the only transformation rules. In this sense, even some of the systems to be introduced in this chapter, such as K and T, are not finitely axiomatizable.

6 The name 'K' was given to this system in Lemmon and Scott (1977), p. 29, in honour of Saul Kripke, from whose work the model theory for normal modal systems is largely derived. K is also sometimes called T°. K was briefly referred to (though not by that name) in *IML* on pp. 301–2. In that work the system T was treated as basic, and K was thought of as obtained from it by dropping the axiom $Lp \supset p$. By contrast, our present approach takes K as basic and regards T as an extension of it.

7 Segerberg (1971), p. 93.

8 Dead ends must not be confused with the non-normal worlds used in the semantics for systems such as S2 (see *IML*, p. 275). In these non-normal worlds $L\alpha$ is always *false* and $M\alpha$ is always *true*, whereas in dead ends the reverse is the case. We shall not be concerned with such non-normal worlds in this book. S2 is not in fact a normal system. A completeness proof for it, using the canonical model method expounded in the next chapter, is, however, given in Cresswell (1982). See also Segerberg (1971) and Routley (1970).

9 The axioms **T** and **4** are the A5 and A7 of *IML* respectively. It is easy to see that **B** is interchangeable as an axiom with $p \supset LMp$, which is used to construct the Brouwerian system in *IML* (pp. 57–8). Similarly, **E** is interchangeable with $Mp \supset LMp$, the A8 of *IML* (p. 49). Sometimes, though not always, we have found it convenient to give the name of a system also to the axiom that is most distinctive of it; we have done this here for **T** and **B**, and we did it earlier on for **K**. A related practice, begun in Lemmon and Scott (1977) and followed in, e.g., Segerberg (1971) and Chellas (1980), is that of naming systems by combining the names of their axioms. The systems T, S4, B and S5 are then called KT, KT4, KTB and KTE respectively. This practice has much to commend it, but for the sake of uniformity with *IML* we shall for the most part retain the more traditional names of the systems.

10 See especially Lemmon and Scott (1977), Segerberg (1971) and Chellas (1980); also, for systems between S4 and S5, Zeman (1973).

11 For some of these results see chapter 4 of *IML*. In *IML* reflexive models were called 'T models', reflexive and transitive ones were called 'S4 models', and so forth. We have thought it better to avoid such terminology here, to avoid confusion with the expressions 'model for T', etc., which we introduce later (p. 49) and which have an importantly different sense.

2 Canonical models and completeness proofs

In the preceding chapter we explained that what we mean by saying that a modal system is complete with respect to a certain class of models is that every wff that is valid in every model in that class is a theorem of that system. We are now going to expound a method of proving completeness which is known as the method of *canonical models*.[1] This is an extremely powerful and flexible technique which can be adapted to a wide range of modal systems. In the present chapter we shall use it to prove the completeness of a number of systems, including K, T, S4, B and S5. Later on we shall apply it to other systems as well.

Completeness and consistency

We begin with some further remarks about the notion of completeness. Suppose that S is a normal modal system, and that we have in mind some class $\mathscr{C}$ of models with respect to which we want to prove that S is complete. Let us call the models in $\mathscr{C}$, for short, $\mathscr{C}$ models, and let us say that a wff is $\mathscr{C}$-*valid* iff it is valid in every $\mathscr{C}$ model. Then to say that S is complete with respect to $\mathscr{C}$ is to say that every $\mathscr{C}$-valid wff is a theorem of S, and clearly this amounts to saying that if any wff is *not* a theorem of S, then it is not $\mathscr{C}$-valid. To put the matter more formally, using the notation '$\vdash_S \alpha$' for 'α is a theorem of S' and '$\nvdash_S \alpha$' for 'α is not a theorem of S', S is complete with respect to a class of models iff

(1) For every wff α, if $\dashv_S \alpha$ then there is some $\mathscr{C}$ model $\langle$ W, R, V $\rangle$ in which for some $w \in$ W, V $(\alpha, w) = 0$.

Next, let us say that a wff α is *S-inconsistent* if its negation is a theorem of S (i.e. if $\vdash_S \sim \alpha$), and that it is *S-consistent* if this is not so (i.e. if $\dashv_S \sim \alpha$). (This means, of course, that we are defining consistency in terms of theoremhood in a system, not in any semantic way, e.g. in terms of models or truth-values.) Now consider the following relation that might obtain between a system and a class $\mathscr{C}$ of models:

(2) For every wff α, if α is S-consistent then there is some $\mathscr{C}$ model $\langle$ W, R, V $\rangle$ in which for some $w \in$ W, V $(\alpha, w) = 1$.

It is not difficult to show that if (2) holds, so does (1). For if $\dashv_S \alpha$, this means that $\sim \alpha$ is S-consistent; so if (2) holds, there is a $\mathscr{C}$ model in which for some $w \in$ W, V $(\sim \alpha, w) = 1$. But by $[V \sim]$, we then have V $(\alpha, w) = 0$, and so (1) holds. (It is equally easy to show that if (1) holds, so does (2); but this is not the result we need at present, and we leave its proof to the reader.)

What the canonical model method directly proves about a system S and a class of models is (2). We have just shown that this also proves (1), and therefore establishes completeness in the sense in which we originally defined it.

We note here that a model in which α is true in at least one world is sometimes called a *verifying model for* α. Using this terminology, we can express (2) more succinctly by saying that every S-consistent wff has a verifying $\mathscr{C}$ model.

We shall now generalize the notion of S-consistency to apply not merely to a single wff but to a set of wff. If Λ is a finite set of wff, we simply identify it with the single wff which is the conjunction of all its members, in the sense that if $\Lambda = \{\alpha_1, \ldots, \alpha_n\}$, we say that Λ is S-consistent iff $\alpha_1 . \ldots . \alpha_n$ is, i.e. iff

$$\dashv_S \sim (\alpha_1 . \ldots . \alpha_n)$$

If Λ is an infinite set, we cannot proceed quite so simply, since there is no such thing as the conjunction of all its members. What we say in this case is that Λ is S-consistent iff every finite subset of Λ is S-consistent; or in other words, iff there is no finite subset $\{\alpha_1, \ldots, \alpha_n\}$ of Λ such that

$$\vdash_S \sim (\alpha_1 . \ldots . \alpha_n)$$

This indeed we shall take as our general definition of S-consistency, since it will clearly cover the case of a finite set, and even the case of a single formula, if we think of it as the set of which it is the only member.

(On p. 4 we introduced the terms 'consistent' and 'inconsistent' as applied to *systems*, by saying that a system is inconsistent iff every wff is a theorem. In the case of normal modal systems, however, and indeed in general for systems that contain PC, it is not difficult to show that a system S is inconsistent in this sense iff it (i.e. the set of all its theorems) is S-inconsistent in the sense we have defined above.)

We have said that what the canonical model method directly proves is (2) above. But it in fact establishes a stronger result than this, namely that if Λ is any S-consistent set of wff, even one that has infinitely many members, then there is a $\mathscr{C}$ model in which all the wff in Λ are true in the same world; in other words,

(3) If Λ is any S-consistent set of wff, then there is a $\mathscr{C}$ model $\langle$ W, R, V $\rangle$ in which for some $w \in$ W, if $\alpha \in \Lambda$ then V $(\alpha, w) = 1$.

(2) is simply the special case of (3) when Λ has only a single member.

Maximal consistent sets of wff

A set Γ of wff is said to be *maximal* iff for every wff α, either $\alpha \in \Gamma$ or $\sim \alpha \in \Gamma$.[2] Γ is said to be *maximal consistent* with respect to a system S (or maximal S-consistent) iff it is both maximal and S-consistent.

We now state some principles about maximal consistent sets. These all hold where S is any normal modal system.

LEMMA 2.1
Suppose that Γ is any maximal consistent set of wff with respect to S. Then
2.1a for any wff α, exactly one member of $\{\alpha, \sim \alpha\}$ is in Γ;
2.1b $\alpha \vee \beta \in \Gamma$ iff either $\alpha \in \Gamma$ or $\beta \in \Gamma$;

2.1c $\alpha.\beta \in \Gamma$ iff both $\alpha \in \Gamma$ and $\beta \in \Gamma$;

2.1d if $\vdash_s \alpha$, then $\alpha \in \Gamma$;

2.1e if $\alpha \in \Gamma$ and $\alpha \supset \beta \in \Gamma$, then $\beta \in \Gamma$;

2.1f if $\alpha \in \Gamma$ and $\vdash_s \alpha \supset \beta$, then $\beta \in \Gamma$.

PROOF

One half of 2.1a, viz. that at least one member of $\{\alpha, \sim \alpha\}$ is in Γ, is directly given by Γ's maximality. The other half, that they are not both in Γ, follows easily from its consistency: for if both were in Γ, then $\{\alpha, \sim \alpha\}$ would be a subset of Γ; but $\{\alpha, \sim \alpha\}$ is inconsistent, since by PC, $\vdash_s \sim (\alpha. \sim \alpha)$; and therefore Γ itself would be inconsistent.

To prove 2.1b, suppose first that $\alpha \vee \beta$ is in Γ but that neither α nor β is. Then by 2.1a, $\sim \alpha$ and $\sim \beta$ would both be in Γ, and hence $\{\alpha \vee \beta, \sim \alpha, \sim \beta\}$ would be a subset of Γ. But this would make Γ inconsistent, since (again by PC) $\vdash_s \sim ((\alpha \vee \beta). \sim \alpha. \sim \beta)$. Suppose next that one of α and β, say α, is in Γ but that $\alpha \vee \beta$ is not. Then $\{\alpha, \sim (\alpha \vee \beta)\}$ would be a subset of Γ. But this would again make Γ inconsistent, since by PC, $\vdash_s \sim (\alpha. \sim (\alpha \vee \beta))$.

The proof of 2.1c is analogous, using the definition of $\alpha.\beta$ as $\sim (\sim \alpha \vee \sim \beta)$.

The proof of 2.1d is simply that if $\vdash_s \alpha$, then $\sim \alpha$ is S-inconsistent. So $\sim \alpha$ cannot be in Γ, and therefore α must be.

2.1e holds because if we had $\alpha \in \Gamma$, $\alpha \supset \beta \in \Gamma$ but not $\beta \in \Gamma$, then $\{\alpha, \alpha \supset \beta, \sim \beta\}$ would be a subset of Γ. But this would make Γ inconsistent, since by PC, $\vdash_s \sim (\alpha.(\alpha \supset \beta). \sim \beta)$.

2.1f follows immediately from 2.1d and 2.1e.

The next result we shall prove is

THEOREM 2.2

Suppose that Λ is an S-consistent set of wff. Then there is a maximal S-consistent set of wff, Γ, such that $\Lambda \subseteq \Gamma$.

(This theorem is sometimes expressed by saying that every S-consistent set of wff can be extended to a maximal S-consistent set, or has a maximal S-consistent extension.)

PROOF

Let us assume that all the wff of modal logic are arranged in some determinate order and labelled $\alpha_1, \alpha_2, \ldots$. We now define a sequence $\Gamma_0, \Gamma_1, \ldots$ of sets of wff in the following way:

(1) Γ_0 is Λ itself.
(2) Given Γ_n, we let Γ_{n+1} be $\Gamma_n \cup \{\alpha_{n+1}\}$ if this is S-consistent, and we let Γ_{n+1} be $\Gamma_n \cup \{\sim \alpha_{n+1}\}$ if $\Gamma_n \cup \{\alpha_{n+1}\}$ is not S-consistent.

We next show that, for any n, if Γ_n is S-consistent, so is Γ_{n+1}. The proof is that if Γ_{n+1} is not S-consistent, this means that neither $\Gamma_n \cup \{\alpha_{n+1}\}$ nor $\Gamma_n \cup \{\sim \alpha_{n+1}\}$ is S-consistent. This in turn means that there are some wff $\beta_1, \ldots, \beta_m$ in Γ_n such that

$$\vdash_S \sim (\beta_1 \cdot \ldots \cdot \beta_m \cdot \alpha_{n+1}) \tag{i}$$

and also some wff $\gamma_1, \ldots, \gamma_k$ in Γ_n such that

$$\vdash_S \sim (\gamma_1 \cdot \ldots \cdot \gamma_k \cdot \sim \alpha_{n+1}) \tag{ii}$$

Now from (i) and (ii) it follows by PC that

$$\vdash_S \sim (\beta_1 \cdot \ldots \cdot \beta_m \cdot \gamma_1 \cdot \ldots \cdot \gamma_k)$$

– i.e. that $\{\beta_1, \ldots, \beta_m, \gamma_1, \ldots, \gamma_k\}$ is S-inconsistent. But this is a subset of Γ_n, and therefore Γ_n is itself S-inconsistent.

Thus by contraposition, if any Γ_n is S-consistent, so is Γ_{n+1}. But Γ_0 (i.e. Λ) is S-consistent by hypothesis. Therefore each Γ_n is S-consistent.

Now let Γ be the union of all the Γ_ns. Then

(a) Γ is S-consistent. For if it were not, then some finite subset of Γ would be S-inconsistent. But clearly every finite subset of Γ is a subset of some Γ_n and we have shown that no Γ_n is S-inconsistent.
(b) Γ is maximal. For consider any wff α_i. By the construction of Γ_i, either $\alpha_i \in \Gamma_i$ or $\sim \alpha_i \in \Gamma_i$; and so, since $\Gamma_i \subseteq \Gamma$, either $\alpha_i \in \Gamma$ or $\sim \alpha_i \in \Gamma$.
(c) $\Lambda \subseteq \Gamma$, since Λ is Γ_0 and $\Gamma_0 \subseteq \Gamma$.

This completes the proof of Theorem 2.2.

All the results we have proved so far depend only on the fact that S contains PC. They therefore hold for any system, whether modal or not, which contains PC. Our next lemma, however, will depend in addition on the modal properties of S.

We first introduce a new piece of notation. Suppose that Λ is any set of wff of modal logic. Then we write '$L^-(\Lambda)$' to denote the set consisting precisely of every wff α for which $L\alpha$ is in Λ. More formally expressed,

$$L^-(\Lambda) = \{\alpha : L\alpha \in \Lambda\}$$

The lemma can now be stated as follows:

LEMMA 2.3
Let S be any normal modal system, and let Λ be an S-consistent set of wff which contains a wff $\sim L\alpha$. Then $L^-(\Lambda) \cup \{\sim\alpha\}$ is S-consistent.

PROOF
We prove the lemma by showing that if $L^-(\Lambda) \cup \{\sim\alpha\}$ is *not* S-consistent, then neither is Λ.

Suppose then that $L^-(\Lambda) \cup \{\sim\alpha\}$ is not S-consistent. This means that there is some finite subset $\{\beta_1, \ldots, \beta_n\}$ of $L^-(\Lambda)$ such that

$$\vdash_S \sim(\beta_1 . \ldots . \beta_n . \sim\alpha)$$

Hence by PC,

$$\vdash_S (\beta_1 . \ldots . \beta_n) \supset \alpha$$

So by DR1 (p. 5),

$$\vdash_S L(\beta_1 . \ldots . \beta_n) \supset L\alpha$$

So by L-distribution and Eq (p. 5),

$$\vdash_S (L\beta_1 . \ldots . L\beta_n) \supset L\alpha$$

And finally, by PC,

$$\vdash_S \sim(L\beta_1 . \ldots . L\beta_n . \sim L\alpha)$$

But this means that $\{L\beta_1, \ldots, L\beta_n, \sim L\alpha\}$ is not S-consistent; so since it is a subset of Λ, Λ is not S-consistent, which is what we had to prove.

The lemma holds for all normal modal systems, since the only modal principles used, viz. DR1 and the law of L-distribution, can be proved in every such system.

This ends the proof.

A useful corollary of Lemma 2.3 is

LEMMA 2.3a

Let S be any normal modal system, and let Λ be an S-consistent set of wff which contains a wff $M\alpha$. Then $L^-(\Lambda) \cup \{\alpha\}$ is S-consistent.[3]

This follows directly from Lemma 2.3, by the definition of M.

Canonical models

Suppose that S is any consistent normal propositional modal system. We are going in a moment to show how to define a special kind of model called the *canonical model* for S. We shall be able to prove that the canonical model for S has the remarkable property that every non-theorem of S is false in some world in it; or, what comes to the same thing, that every S-consistent wff is true in some world in it. We shall prove this quite generally for any normal system. Now we showed on p. 17 that a system S is complete with respect to a class, $\mathscr{C}$, of models if for every S-consistent wff there is some $\mathscr{C}$ model in which it is true in some world. So if we can also prove, in the case of a particular normal system S, that its canonical model is a $\mathscr{C}$ model, it follows immediately that S is complete with respect to the class of $\mathscr{C}$ models.

(To be sure, in order to prove the completeness of S it is not necessary to exhibit a single $\mathscr{C}$ model which will verify every S-consistent formula at once. It would be sufficient to show that for each S-consistent formula there is *some* $\mathscr{C}$ model which verifies it. But clearly a single $\mathscr{C}$ model which verifies them all will serve the purpose, and serve it very efficiently.)

The canonical model for S is, like any other model for a normal propositional modal system, a triple $\langle W, R, V \rangle$. To define it, we have to say what the members of W are, specify which pairs of members of W are related by R, and lay down the truth-value of each variable at each member of W.

We noted on p. 7 that although we have usually referred to the members of W in a model as 'worlds', they can be any kinds of objects we choose. In a canonical model we take *sets of wff* as our worlds; and in the canonical model for a normal propositional modal system S, the members of W are to be all and only those sets of wff which are maximal consistent with respect to S.

To define R we stipulate that if w and w' are any members of

W, then we have $w\mathbf{R}w'$ iff, for every wff α, if $L\alpha$ is in w, α itself is in w'. To use the notation we introduced earlier, $w\mathbf{R}w'$ iff $L^-(w) \subseteq w'$. Finally, we lay it down that any variable is to count as true in a world w if it is a member of w, and false in w if it is not.

Thus for any normal propositional modal system S, its canonical model $\langle W, R, V \rangle$ is defined as follows:

(1) $W = \{w : w$ is a maximal S-consistent set of wff$\}$.

(2) For any $w, w' \in W$, $w\mathbf{R}w'$ iff $L^-(w) \subseteq w'$.

(3) For any variable p and any $w \in W$, $V(p, w) = 1$ if $p \in w$; otherwise $V(p, w) = 0$.

The rules $[V \sim]$, $[V \vee]$, $[VL]$, etc. of course hold as usual, since they are invariant elements in our model theory for normal systems.

We said a few paragraphs back that we would be able to prove that every S-consistent wff is true in some world in the canonical model for S. To do so, we shall first prove what is sometimes called the *fundamental theorem for canonical models* (for normal modal systems), which is to the effect that in a canonical model every wff – and not merely every variable – is true in a world w if it is a member of w, and false in w if it is not. It is easy to see how this will give us the result we want. For if α is an S-consistent wff, then Theorem 2.2 assures us that α is a member of some maximal S-consistent set of wff w; our definition of W ensures that this w will be a member of W in the canonical model; and the fundamental theorem will then show that α is true in w.

As we also noted, the completeness of a particular system then follows if we can show that its canonical model actually is a model in the specified class. But in the meantime we state and prove the fundamental theorem:

THEOREM 2.4
Let $\langle W, R, V \rangle$ be the canonical model for a normal propositional modal system S. Then for any wff α and any $w \in W$, $V(\alpha, w) = 1$ if $\alpha \in w$ and $V(\alpha, w) = 0$ if $\alpha \notin w$.

PROOF
The proof is by induction on the construction of a wff of modal logic. We first note that if α is a variable, the theorem holds by

clause (3) in the definition of a canonical model. We then prove (a) that if the theorem holds for a wff α, it also holds for $\sim \alpha$, (b) that if it holds for each of a pair of wff α and β, it holds for $\alpha \vee \beta$, and (c) that if it holds for a wff α, it also holds for $L\alpha$. Since $\sim$, $\vee$ and L are our only primitive operators, this will show that the theorem holds for every wff.

We now prove each of (a) – (c) in turn.

(a) Consider a wff $\sim \alpha$ and any $w \in W$. By $[V \sim]$ we have

$$V(\sim \alpha, w) = 1 \text{ iff } V(\alpha, w) = 0.$$

Since the theorem is assumed to hold for α, we have

$$V(\alpha, w) = 0 \text{ iff } \alpha \notin w.$$

Hence we have

$$V(\sim \alpha, w) = 1 \text{ iff } \alpha \notin w.$$

But by Lemma 2.1a, $\alpha \notin w$ iff $\sim \alpha \in w$. Hence finally we have

$$V(\sim \alpha, w) = 1 \text{ iff } \sim \alpha \in w$$

as required.

(b) Consider next $\alpha \vee \beta$. By $[V \vee]$ we have

$$V(\alpha \vee \beta, w) = 1 \text{ iff either } V(\alpha, w) = 1 \text{ or } V(\beta, w) = 1.$$

Since the theorem is assumed to hold for α and for β, we therefore have

$$V(\alpha \vee \beta, w) = 1 \text{ iff either } \alpha \in w \text{ or } \beta \in w.$$

Hence by Lemma 2.1b we have

$$V(\alpha \vee \beta, w) = 1 \text{ iff } \alpha \vee \beta \in w$$

as required.

(c) Consider finally $L\alpha$.

(A) Suppose that $L\alpha \in w$. Then by the definition of R we have $\alpha \in w'$ for every w' such that $w R w'$. Since the theorem is assumed to hold for α, we therefore have $V(\alpha, w') = 1$ for each such w'. Hence by $[VL]$, $V(L\alpha, w) = 1$.

(B) Suppose now that $L\alpha \notin w$. Then by Lemma 2.1a, $\sim L\alpha \in w$. Hence by Lemma 2.3, $L^-(w) \cup \{\sim \alpha\}$ is S-consistent. So by

Theorem 2.2 and the definition of W, there is some $w' \in$ W such that $L^-(w) \cup \{ \sim \alpha \} \subseteq w'$, and therefore such that (i) $L^-(w) \subseteq w'$ and (ii) $\sim \alpha \in w'$. Now (i) gives us wRw', by the definition of R. And since the theorem is assumed to hold for α, and therefore, by (a) above, also for $\sim \alpha$, (ii) gives us $V(\sim \alpha, w') = 1$, and hence $V(\alpha, w') \neq 1$. So by [VL] we have $V(L\alpha, w) \neq 1$.

This completes the proof of Theorem 2.4.

COROLLARY 2.5
Any wff α is valid in the canonical model for S iff $\vdash_S \alpha$.

PROOF
Let $\langle$ W, R, V $\rangle$ be the canonical model for S. Suppose that $\vdash_S \alpha$. Then by Lemma 2.1d, α is in every maximal S-consistent set of wff. Hence α is in every $w \in$ W, and so by Theorem 2.4, $V(\alpha, w) = 1$ for every $w \in$ W; i.e. α is valid in $\langle$ W, R, V $\rangle$. Suppose now that $\dashv_S \alpha$. Then $\sim \alpha$ is S-consistent. Therefore for some $w \in$ W, $\sim \alpha \in w$, and hence $\alpha \notin w$. So by Theorem 2.4, $V(\alpha, w) \neq 1$ for some $w \in$ W; i.e. α is not valid in $\langle$ W, R, V $\rangle$.

We conclude this section with three further results which will simplify some proofs later on.

Where Λ is any set of wff, let us write '$M^+(\Lambda)$' to denote the set of wff obtained by prefixing M to every wff in Λ; i.e.

$$M^+(\Lambda) = \{M\alpha : \alpha \in \Lambda\}$$

Then the first of our three results is

THEOREM 2.6
Suppose that Γ and Γ' are maximal consistent sets of wff with respect to a normal modal system. Then $L^-(\Gamma) \subseteq \Gamma'$ iff $M^+(\Gamma') \subseteq \Gamma$.

PROOF
(A) Suppose that (i) $L^-(\Gamma) \subseteq \Gamma'$ but (ii) $M^+(\Gamma') \nsubseteq \Gamma$. Then by (ii), there is some wff $\alpha \in \Gamma'$ such that $M\alpha \notin \Gamma$. Hence $\sim M\alpha \in \Gamma$, and so (by LMI) $L \sim \alpha \in \Gamma$. Therefore by (i), $\sim \alpha \in \Gamma'$; and so $\alpha \notin \Gamma'$, contrary to our assumption.
(B) Suppose now that (iii) $M^+(\Gamma') \subseteq \Gamma$ but (iv) $L^-(\Gamma) \nsubseteq \Gamma'$. Then by (iv), there is some wff $L\alpha \in \Gamma$ such that $\alpha \notin \Gamma'$, and so $\sim \alpha \in \Gamma'$. Hence by (iii) $M \sim \alpha \in \Gamma$; so (by LMI) $\sim L\alpha \in \Gamma$; so $L\alpha \notin \Gamma$, again contrary to our assumption.

This ends the proof.

Note that in virtue of Theorem 2.6 we could equally well have defined R in a canonical model by replacing clause (2) by

(2') For any $w, w' \in W$, wRw' iff $M^+(w') \subseteq w$.

And in any case, if in any canonical model we have wRw', then for any wff $\alpha \in w'$, $M\alpha \in w$.

A straightforward generalization of the proof of Theorem 2.6 yields our second result:

COROLLARY 2.7
Suppose that Γ and Γ' are maximal consistent sets of wff with respect to a normal modal system. Then for any natural number $n(\geqslant 0)$, $\{\alpha : L^n\alpha \in \Gamma\} \subseteq \Gamma'$ iff $\{M^n\alpha : \alpha \in \Gamma'\} \subseteq \Gamma$.

Our final result in this section is a kind of generalization of the definition of R in a canonical model:

THEOREM 2.8
Let $\langle W, R, V \rangle$ be the canonical model for a normal modal system. Then for any w and $w' \in W$, and for any natural number n ($\geqslant 0$), wR^nw' iff $\{\alpha : L^n\alpha \in w\} \subseteq w'$ (or equivalently, by Corollary 2.7, iff $\{M^n\alpha : \alpha \in w'\} \subseteq w$).

PROOF
It is a straightforward consequence of the definition of R in a canonical model that if wR^nw' then $\{\alpha : L^n\alpha \in w\} \subseteq w'$.

For the converse we have to show that, for every $n \geqslant 0$,

(A) For any w and $w' \in W$, if $\{\alpha : L^n\alpha \in w\} \subseteq w'$, then wR^nw'.

We prove this inductively, by showing that (A) holds when $n = 0$, and then that, on the hypothesis that it holds for an arbitrary natural number n, it also holds for $n + 1$.

If $n = 0$, then $\{\alpha : L^n\alpha \in w\}$ is simply $\{\alpha : \alpha \in w\}$, i.e. w itself. So if $\{\alpha : L^n\alpha \in w\} \subseteq w'$, then $w \subseteq w'$. Since w and w' are maximal consistent sets, it follows that $w = w'$, i.e. that wR^0w'.

We now take as our induction hypothesis that (A) holds for n. We assume that for some pair of worlds, w and $w^* \in W$, $\{\alpha : L^{n+1}\alpha \in w\} \subseteq w^*$, and we want to show that in that case $wR^{n+1}w^*$. Clearly it will suffice to show that there is some $w_1 \in W$ such that wRw_1 and $w_1R^nw^*$. And for this it will suffice to show that

(Λ) $L^-(w) \cup \{\sim L^n\alpha : \alpha \notin w^*\}$

is consistent. For if Λ is consistent, there will be a world $w_1 \in W$ which includes it. It is easy to see that wRw_1, since $L^-(w) \subseteq w_1$; and it is not hard to show that $w_1 R^n w^*$. For if this were not the case, then by the induction hypothesis there would have to be a wff α such that $L^n\alpha \in w_1$ but $\alpha \notin w^*$. However, by the definition of Λ, if $\alpha \notin w^*$, $\sim L^n\alpha \in \Lambda$; so we should have $\sim L^n\alpha \in w_1$ and therefore $L^n\alpha \notin w_1$.

All that is needed, therefore, is to prove that Λ is consistent. Suppose, then, that it is not. Then for some $L\beta_1, \ldots, L\beta_j \in w$ and some $\alpha_1, \ldots, \alpha_k \notin w^*$,

$$\vdash \sim (\beta_1 \ldots \beta_j . \sim L^n\alpha_1 \ldots \sim L^n\alpha_k)$$

Hence by PC, DR1 and L-distribution, as in the proof of Lemma 2.3,

$$\vdash (L\beta_1 \ldots L\beta_j) \supset L(L^n\alpha_1 \vee \ldots \vee L^n\alpha_k)$$

Hence by repeated applications of $(Lp \vee Lq) \supset L(p \vee q)$,

$$\vdash (L\beta_1 \ldots L\beta_j) \supset L^{n+1}(\alpha_1 \vee \ldots \vee \alpha_k)$$

But each of $L\beta_1, \ldots, L\beta_j \in w$. Therefore $L^{n+1}(a_1 \vee \ldots \vee \alpha_k) \in w$. But $\{\alpha : L^{n+1}\alpha \in w\} \subseteq w^*$. Therefore $\alpha_1 \vee \ldots \vee \alpha_k \in w^*$, which contradicts the assumption that none of $\alpha_1, \ldots, \alpha_k$ is in w^*.

This shows that Λ is consistent, and thus completes the proof of Theorem 2.8.[4]

The completeness of K, T, S4, B and S5

Let us take stock of the position we have now reached.

We assume we have a normal modal system S and a class of models $\mathscr{C}$. To say that S is complete (with respect to that class of models) is to say that every $\mathscr{C}$-valid wff – i.e. every wff that is valid in every $\mathscr{C}$ model – is a theorem of S. Clearly this is equivalent to saying that every wff which is *not* a theorem of S is invalid in some $\mathscr{C}$ model. So let us take any wff α that is not a theorem of S. By Corollary 2.5, α is invalid in the canonical model for S. Therefore *if the canonical model for S is a $\mathscr{C}$ model*, there will in fact be some $\mathscr{C}$ model, namely the canonical model itself, in which α is invalid.

This should make it clear that in order to prove the completeness of a particular normal system S, the only step we still have to fill in is the one just italicized, namely that the canonical model for S is a $\mathscr{C}$ model. In other words, any normal system for which this is so is complete.

This means that we have immediately a completeness result for K with respect to the class of all models (which is the class with respect to which we previously showed that K is sound). The proof simply consists in the obvious fact that the canonical model for K is a model.

THEOREM 2.9
T is complete with respect to the class of all reflexive models.

PROOF
All we have to prove is that in the canonical model for T, R is reflexive, i.e. that for every $w \in W$, wRw. By the definition of R in a canonical model, what wRw means is that $L^-(w) \subseteq w$, i.e. that for any wff α, if $L\alpha$ is in w, so is α itself. The proof of this is simply that by the axiom T and US, $\vdash_T L\alpha \supset \alpha$ for every wff α. So by Lemma 2.1f, if $L\alpha \in w$, $\alpha \in w$.

THEOREM 2.10
S4 is complete with respect to the class of all reflexive transitive models.

PROOF
What we have to prove is that in the canonical model for S4, (a) wRw for every $w \in W$, and (b) if $w_1 R w_2$ and $w_2 R w_3$ then $w_1 R w_3$, for any $w_1, w_2, w_3 \in W$. (a) is proved as for T. The proof of (b) is as follows. What we have to show is that if $L^-(w_1) \subseteq w_2$ and $L^-(w_2) \subseteq w_3$, then $L^-(w_1) \subseteq w_3$ (i.e. whenever $L\alpha \in w_1$, $\alpha \in w_3$). Suppose then that $L\alpha \in w_1$. Then since $\vdash_{S4} L\alpha \supset LL\alpha$, we have $LL\alpha \in w_1$ by Lemma 2.1f. Hence since $L^-(w_1) \subseteq w_2$, $L\alpha \in w_2$; and since $L^-(w_2) \subseteq w_3, \alpha \in w_3$.

(Note that step (b) gives us a proof that the system K4 mentioned on p. 11 is complete with respect to the class of all models in which R is transitive, whether or not it is also reflexive. It is also a straightforward matter to show that K4 is sound with respect to this class of models.)

THEOREM 2.11
B is complete with respect to the class of all reflexive symmetrical models.

PROOF

(a) Since B contains T, the proof that R in the canonical model for B is reflexive is again as for T. (b) The proof that it is also symmetrical is as follows. We have to show that for any $w_1, w_2 \in W$, if $w_1 R w_2$ then $w_2 R w_1$, which means that if $L^-(w_1) \subseteq w_2$, then $L^-(w_2) \subseteq w_1$. So suppose that $L^-(w_1) \subseteq w_2$. To prove that in that case we have $L^-(w_2) \subseteq w_1$, we show that if $\alpha \notin w_1$, $L\alpha \notin w_2$. Suppose then that $\alpha \notin w_1$. Then by Lemma 2.1a, $\sim \alpha \in w_1$. Therefore since $\vdash_B \sim \alpha \supset L \sim L\alpha$, $L \sim L\alpha \in w_1$, by Lemma 2.1f. But by hypothesis, $L^-(w_1) \subseteq w_2$, so $\sim L\alpha \in w_2$. Hence by Lemma 2.1a again, $L\alpha \notin w_2$, as required.

(Step (b) shows that KB is complete with respect to the class of all symmetrical models; and soundness is again easy to prove.)

THEOREM 2.12

S5 is complete with respect to the class of all models in which R is an equivalence relation.

PROOF

An equivalence relation is one which is reflexive, transitive and symmetrical. Now the axioms **T**, **4** and **B** can all easily be shown to be theorems of S5, so the present theorem follows from the proofs given for Theorems 2.9–2.11.

Three further systems

Partly in order to illustrate the flexibility of the canonical model method and partly for the sake of developments in later chapters, we shall now give completeness proofs for three other systems.

The first example is a system often called D, which is obtained by adding to K the axiom

D $\quad Lp \supset Mp$

D is intermediate between **K** and T.[5]

The models with respect to which we shall prove D to be complete are those in which the relation R is *serial*. What this means is that for every $w \in W$, there is some $w' \in W$ (not necessarily w itself) such that wRw'; in other words, the model has no dead ends in the sense explained on p. 9. It is easy to see that $Lp \supset Mp$ is valid in all models in which R is serial, and therefore that D is sound with respect to the class of all such models. For if Lp is true in any world w, then p is true in all worlds that w can see; but if there is even one such world, as there must be if R is serial, that is enough to make Mp also true at w.

For completeness we have to prove that in the canonical model for D, R is serial. Consider any $w \in$ W in this canonical model. Take any wff $L\alpha$ in w (and N guarantees that there will be infinitely many such wff). Then by the axiom **D** and Lemma 2.1f, $M\alpha$ is in w. Hence by Lemma 2.3a, $L^-(w) \cup \{\alpha\}$ is consistent, and so there will be some $w' \in$ W which contains it. Since $L^-(w) \subseteq w'$, we have wRw'; and therefore R is serial.

Our second example is the system S4.3, which is S4 with the additional axiom

D1 $L(Lp \supset q) \lor L(Lq \supset p)$

This system was discussed in *IML* on pp.262ff. and 289f., and will be dealt with in greater detail later on, in chapters 5 and 7. It can be shown to be characterized by the class of all models in which R is reflexive, transitive, and *connected* in the sense that, for any w_1, w_2 and $w_3 \in$ W,

If $w_1 Rw_2$ and $w_1 Rw_3$, then either $w_2 Rw_3$ or $w_3 Rw_2$.

We leave the proof of soundness – which is straightforward – to the reader, and proceed to the completeness proof.

Since S4.3 contains S4, we know from the proof of Theorem 2.7 that R is reflexive and transitive in the canonical model for S4.3. So all that remains to be done in order to prove completeness is to show that it is also connected. In other words, we have to show that it is impossible to have the following situation for any w_1, w_2, w_3 in the canonical model for S4.3:

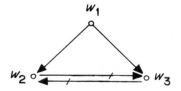

(where $w \to w'$ means that wRw', and $w \nrightarrow w'$ means that not wRw').

The proof is this. Suppose that such a situation were to obtain somewhere in the canonical model for S4.3. Then since w_2 cannot see w_3 (i.e. $L^-(w_2) \nsubseteq w_3$), there must be some wff α such that

(1) $L\alpha \in w_2$ but (2) $\alpha \notin w_3$.

Similarly, since w_3 cannot see w_2, there must be some wff β such that

(3) $L\beta \in w_3$ but (4) $\beta \notin w_2$.

But (1) and (4) give us

(5) $L\alpha \supset \beta \notin w_2$

(since if both $L\alpha$ and $L\alpha \supset \beta$ were in w_2, we should have $\beta \in w_2$ by Lemma 2.1e, contrary to (4)); and similarly, (3) and (2) give us

(6) $L\beta \supset \alpha \notin w_3$.

Next, since $w_1 R w_2$, (5) gives us, by the definition of R,

(7) $L(L\alpha \supset \beta) \notin w_1$;

and since $w_1 R w_3$, (6) similarly gives us

(8) $L(L\beta \supset \alpha) \notin w_1$.

Finally, (7) and (8), by Lemma 2.1b, give

(9) $L(L\alpha \supset \beta) \vee L(L\beta \supset \alpha) \notin w_1$.

This, however, is impossible, since this wff is a substitution-instance of **D1** and therefore must be in every world in the canonical model for S4.3. So the situation envisaged in the diagram cannot arise.

This establishes the completeness of S4.3.

Our third example is the system S4.2, which is S4 with the additional axiom

G1 $MLp \supset LMp$

The relevant models are those in which R is reflexive, transitive, and *convergent* in the sense that, for any $w_1, w_2, w_3 \in W$,

If $w_1 R w_2$ and $w_1 R w_3$, then there is some $w_4 \in W$ such that both $w_2 R w_4$ and $w_3 R w_4$.

We again leave the soundness proof to the reader, and proceed to the completeness proof.

As in the case of S4.3, the fact that S4.2 contains S4 shows that R is reflexive and transitive in the canonical model for S4.2. So in order to prove completeness, all we still have to do is to show that it is convergent. In other words, we have to show that wherever the following pattern occurs in the canonical model for S4.2

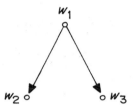

there is always a world w_4 in the model which continues the pattern in this way:

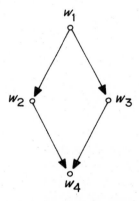

To prove this, it is sufficient to show that the set of wff

$$(\Lambda) \quad L^-(w_2) \cup L^-(w_3)$$

is S4.2-consistent. For if it is, then it will be included in some set w' which is maximal S4.2-consistent and is therefore in the canonical model; and since both $L^-(w_2) \subseteq w'$ and $L^-(w_3) \subseteq w'$, we shall have both $w_2 R w'$ and $w_3 R w'$. So this w' can be our required w_4.

Suppose, then, that Λ is not S4.2-consistent. What this means is that there are wff $L\alpha_1, \ldots, L\alpha_n$ in w_2 and wff $L\beta_1, \ldots, L\beta_m$ in w_3 such that

$$\vdash_{S4.2} \sim (\alpha_1 . \ldots . \alpha_n . \beta_1 . \ldots . \beta_m)$$

By Lemma 2.1c and L-distribution, we can express this more succinctly by saying that for some $L\alpha \in w_2$ and some $L\beta \in w_3$,

$$\vdash_{S4.2} \sim (\alpha . \beta)$$

By PC this gives us

$$\vdash_{S4.2} \alpha \supset \sim \beta$$

and hence, by DR3 and LMI (p. 5),

$$(1) \quad \vdash_{S4.2} M\alpha \supset \sim L\beta$$

Now since $L\alpha \in w_2$, and $w_1 R w_2$, we have $ML\alpha \in w_1$ by Theorem 2.6. Hence by **G1** we have $LM\alpha \in w_1$. But $w_1 R w_3$; so $M\alpha \in w_3$. Hence by (1) we have $\sim L\beta \in w_3$. But this is impossible, since by hypothesis, $L\beta \in w_3$.

Thus the supposition that Λ is inconsistent has been disproved, and S4.2 has therefore been shown to be complete.

It should be noted that in our proofs that **R** is connected in the canonical model for S4.3 and convergent in that for S4.2, we appealed only to **D1** or **G1** in addition to the principles common to all normal systems, and made no use of any theorems that depend on **T** or **4**. This shows that the system **K + D1** is complete for models in which **R** is connected, and **K + G1** for those in which it is convergent, irrespective of whether it is also reflexive or transitive.

Dead ends

We remarked on p. 9 that a model may contain worlds that are not related to any worlds at all, not even to themselves, and we called such worlds *dead ends*. We also noted that if w is a dead end in any model, then $V(L\alpha, w) = 1$ and $V(M\alpha, w) = 0$, for any wff α whatsoever.

One thing that follows from this is that **K** has no theorems of the form $M\alpha$. For as we have seen, every theorem of **K** is valid in every model without exception; but we have only to produce a model in which some world is a dead end to find that $M\alpha$ is false at that world and therefore is not valid in that model. For the same reason, of course, K has no theorems of the form $\sim L\alpha$.

We could in fact add to K *any* axiom of the form $L\alpha$, and the resulting system would still be consistent. The strongest system we could form in this way would be obtained by adding the axiom Lp, for then by US every wff of the form $L\alpha$ – even $L(p. \sim p)$ – would be a theorem. This system has been called the *Verum* system (*Ver* for short). That it is consistent can be shown as follows. Consider the class $\mathscr{C}$ of models in which every world is a dead end. Obviously all the theorems of K are $\mathscr{C}$-valid; moreover, so is Lp, since it is of the form $L\alpha$. As in other cases, the transformation rules preserve validity; so Ver is sound with respect to $\mathscr{C}$. Clearly, however, we can have a world in a model in $\mathscr{C}$ in which p is false. So Ver does not have p as a theorem, and this is enough to ensure its consistency.

To prove that Ver is also complete with respect to this class of models, we first prove a lemma which will also be useful later on.

LEMMA 2.13

For any model $\langle$ W, R, V $\rangle$ and any $w \in$ W, $V(L(p. \sim p), w) = 1$ iff w is a dead end.

PROOF

Suppose that w is a dead end. Then $V(L\alpha, w) = 1$ for every wff α. Hence, in particular, $V(L(p. \sim p), w) = 1$. For the converse, suppose that $V(L(p. \sim p), w) = 1$. If w is *not* a dead end, there is some $w' \in$ W such that wRw'. But then, by [VL], we shall have $V(p. \sim p, w') = 1$. This, however, is impossible, since $V(p. \sim p, w') = 0$ for every w' in every model. Therefore w must be a dead end.

THEOREM 2.14

Ver is characterized by the class of all models in which every world is a dead end.

PROOF

We have already shown that Ver is sound with respect to this class of models. To show that it is also complete it is sufficient to prove that in the canonical model for Ver every world is a dead end. The proof of this is simply that since $L(p. \sim p)$ is a theorem of

Ver, we have $L(p. \sim p) \in w$, and hence $V(L(p. \sim p), w) = 1$, for every $w \in W$ in the canonical model for Ver. So by Lemma 2.13, every such w is a dead end.

The Verum system may appear bizarre in many ways, and it certainly seems to impose some strain on the attempt to interpret L as meaning 'necessarily'. Nevertheless it has two interesting characteristics which are worth calling attention to.

First, on p. 59 of *IML* it was noted that the addition of $p \supset Lp$ to T (or, what comes to the same thing, the addition of $p \equiv Lp$ to K) renders L and M redundant and gives us a system which 'collapses into PC'. To put this in another way, L then becomes the truth-functor which gives $L\alpha$ the same truth-value as α itself has. Such a truth-functor is in a sense a 'vacuous' or 'trivial' one, and for this reason $K + p \equiv Lp$ is often called the *Trivial* system (or *Triv* for short). Now the Verum system provides another way (in fact the only other way) in which a normal modal system can collapse into PC; for in Ver, L may also be thought of as a truth-functor, though this time as the one which makes a true proposition out of any proposition whatsoever. In fact, just as in Triv every wff is equivalent to the PC wff that results from deleting all the Ls and Ms in it, so in Ver every wff is equivalent to the PC wff that results from replacing every sub-formula of the form $L\alpha$ in it by $p \supset p$, and every sub-formula of the form $M\alpha$ by $p. \sim p$. However, while T can collapse into PC by way of Triv – i.e. by adding the axiom $p \supset Lp$ to it – it cannot do so by way of Ver, since the addition of Lp to T would immediately give us p as a theorem, and thus result in an inconsistent system. In fact, Lp cannot consistently be added to any system which contains the system D that was discussed on pp. 29f.

Secondly, both Triv and Ver have the property of *Post-completeness* which was referred to (under the name 'strong completeness') on p. 19 of *IML*, and are in fact the only normal systems that have this property. What this means is that in the case of these two systems, but no others, no wff that is not already a theorem can be added without inconsistency resulting. To put it in another way, these two systems, and only these, have no consistent proper extensions. Every normal system, indeed, is either contained in Triv or contained in Ver, though many of them, such as K itself or K4, are contained in both. Moreover, every normal system which contains D is contained in Triv; and every one that does not contain D is contained in Ver.[6]

There is also an interesting parallel between the semantics for Ver and for Triv. Ver, as we have seen, is characterized by the class of all models in which every world is a dead end. Triv is characterized by the class of all models in which every world is related to itself and only to itself. In each case, each world is isolated from every other world.

Suppose, next, that instead of adding Lp to K, we were to add LLp. In that case we should have a system which is *weaker* than Ver. We might call it Ver_2, and rename the Verum system Ver_1. Clearly we can derive LLp from Lp by substituting Lp for p; but we cannot obtain Lp as a theorem of Ver_2. (If we feel it to be strange that LLp is a weaker formula than Lp, this may be because we are forgetting that in these systems we do not have the T axiom $Lp \supset p$.) It is not difficult to show that Ver_2 is characterized by the class of models in which if any world is not itself a dead end, then every world it can see *is* a dead end.

We can generalize this result as follows: For any $n \geqslant 1$, let us call the system $K + L^n p$, Ver_n. Then the Ver_n systems form an infinite sequence in descending order of strength, with Ver_1 at the top. And each Ver_n is characterized by the class of models in which everything that any world can see in $n - 1$ steps is a dead end; i.e. more formally, for any w and $w' \in W$

$$wR^{n-1}w' \supset \sim (\exists u)w'Ru$$

We leave the proof of this to the reader as an exercise.

Finally, we shall consider models in which every world either is itself a dead end or can see at least one dead end, though we do not now insist, as we did in the case of Ver_2, that *every* world that any world can see is a dead end. In other words, we are considering the condition that, for every $w \in W$,

$$\sim (\exists w')wRw' \vee (\exists w')(wRw'. \sim (\exists u)w'Ru)$$

The system characterized by the class of such models we shall call the *M-Verum* system (MV), since it can be thought of as a kind of 'possibility' variant of Ver. It can be axiomatized as K_+

MV $MLp \vee Lp$[7]

It is easy to show that **MV** is valid in all models of the kind we are considering. For if w is a dead end, then Lp is true at w, and hence so is $MLp \vee Lp$. And if w can see some dead end w', then Lp is true at w', and hence MLp is true at w, so once more we have $MLp \vee Lp$ true at w.

As a preliminary to proving completeness we shall first prove

LEMMA 2.15
For any model $\langle W, R, V \rangle$ and any $w \in W$, $V(ML(p. \sim p), w) = 1$ iff there is some $w' \in W$ such that wRw' and w' is a dead end.

PROOF
By $[VM]$, $V(ML(p. \sim p), w) = 1$ iff there is some $w' \in W$ such that wRw' and $V(L(p. \sim p), w') = 1$. But by Lemma 2.13, $V(L(p. \sim p), w') = 1$ iff w' is a dead end.

THEOREM 2.16
MV is characterized by the class of all models in which every world either is a dead end or is related to some dead end.

PROOF
Soundness has already been proved. For completeness it is sufficient to show that in the canonical model for MV, every $w \in W$ is either a dead end or is related to some dead end. We first note that by substituting $p. \sim p$ for p in **MV** we obtain

(1) $ML(p. \sim p) \vee L(p. \sim p)$

Therefore (1) is in every $w \in W$ in the canonical model for MV, and hence, by Lemma 2.1b, so is either $ML(p. \sim p)$ or $L(p. \sim p)$. But if $ML(p. \sim p) \in w$, then by Lemma 2.15, w can see some dead end; and if $L(p. \sim p) \in w$, then by Lemma 2.13, w is itself a dead end.

This proves the theorem.

An interesting point to notice about formula (1) above, or its obvious equivalent, by PC and LMI,

(2) $LM(p \supset p) \supset L(p. \sim p)$

is that its truth-value in any world in any model is completely independent of the value-assignment to the variables, since $p. \sim p$ is bound to be false in every world, and $p \supset p$ is bound to be true in every world, no matter what the value-assignment V may be.

This means that (1) and (2) will be true in any world in *any* model iff that world either is a dead end or can see some dead end.

Moreover, not merely are (1) and (2) theorems of MV, but either of them could be used in place of **MV** as an axiom for the system. We therefore have the result that any model is a model in which all theorems of MV are valid iff every world in it either is a dead end or can see one. We shall return to MV in chapter 4, and this last-mentioned fact about it will then become important.

Exercises – 2

2.1 Prove the soundness, and use canonical models to prove the completeness, of the following systems with respect to the classes of models in which R satisfies the stated conditions.

(a) KB (i.e. K + $\sim p \supset L \sim Lp$). Condition: Symmetry.

(b) KE (i.e. K + $\sim Lp \supset L \sim Lp$). Condition: If $w_1 R w_2$ and $w_1 R w_3$, then $w_2 R w_3$.

(c) S4 + $MLp \supset (p \supset Lp)$.   Conditions: (i)   Reflexiveness; (ii) transitivity; (iii) if $w_1 R w_2$ and $w_1 \neq w_2$, then for every w_3, if $w_1 R w_3$, $w_3 R w_2$. (Hint: for condition (iii) in the completeness proof, first prove that $MLp \supset (q \supset L(p \lor q))$ is a theorem.)

(d) T + $Lp \supset LMLp$. Conditions: (i) Reflexiveness; (ii) if $w_1 R w_2$, then there is some w_3 such that both (1) $w_2 R w_3$ and (2) for any w_4, if $w_3 R w_4$ then $w_1 R w_4$. (Hint: for condition (ii) in the completeness proof, assume that $w_1 R w_2$, show that $L^-(w_2) \cup \{L\alpha : L\alpha \in w_1\}$ is consistent, and let w_3 be a world that includes this set. Ask yourself how this will give the desired result.)

2.2 Prove that every symmetrical relation is convergent. Prove that **G1** is a theorem of KB. Explain the connection between these two results.

2.3 Prove that every reflexive connected relation is convergent. Prove that **G1** is a theorem of T + **D1**. Explain the connection between these two results.

2.4 Prove that the Trivial system is characterized by the class of all models in which every world is related to itself and only to itself. (See p. 35.)

2.5 Prove that K + $p \supset Lp$ is characterized by the class of all models in which every world is either a dead end or is related only to itself.

2.6 Prove that $K + Mp \supset Lp$ is characterized by the class of all models in which every world is related to at most one world (possibly itself).

2.7 Prove that MV may be axiomatized
(a) as $K + ML(p. \sim p) \vee L(p. \sim p)$
(b) as $K + MLp \vee Lq$

Notes

1 This method derives from the work of Lemmon and Scott (1977), and has come to be widely used in recent years. It has much in common with the method of proving completeness given in chapter 9 of *IML*, in that both are based on the idea of maximal consistent sets of wff. There are, however, some important differences between the two methods, as will become clear in chapter 7.

2 This definition of maximality differs from the one given on p. 151 of *IML*, though not in any way that affects which sets count as maximal consistent. In effect we are here taking as our definition something that in *IML* was proved as a result (Lemma 2, p. 153), using the definition given there. Note that maximality, as we now define it, is not system-relative.

3 This is in essence Lemma 4 on p. 155 of *IML*, though we can now note that it holds for all normal systems, not merely for those that contain T.

4 This proof follows essentially the lines of that given in Lemmon and Scott (1977), pp. 32f.

5 The system D, though not by that name, was mentioned briefly on p. 301 of *IML*. The name 'D' derives from the word 'deontic'. In a deontic logic the necessity operator is taken to mean 'it ought to be the case that', and the possibility operator, correspondingly, as 'it is permissible for it to be the case that'. With this interpretation, $Lp \supset p$ ('whatever ought to be the case is the case') is intuitively implausible, but $Lp \supset Mp$ ('whatever ought to be the case is permissible') is intuitively plausible. See Lemmon and Scott (1977), p. 5. This use of 'D' should not be confused with its use as an alternative name for the system S4.3.1 (see *IML*, pp. 262f.).

6 These results are covered by ones obtained by Makinson (1971). See also Segerberg (1972).

7 MV is equivalent to the system which Segerberg (1971), p. 93, calls KW_0. In formulating this system Segerberg uses a constant false proposition ($\perp$) and a constant true proposition ($\top$), and defines the system as $K +$

$$\mathbf{W}_0 \quad LM \top \supset L \perp$$

This axiom is in effect our formula (2), p. 37. He notes that if we interpret L as 'it always will be the case that', then $\mathbf{W}_0$ expresses the idea that time has a last moment. It is perhaps easiest to see why this is so if we recast $\mathbf{W}_0$ as $ML\bot \vee L\bot$. For $L\bot$ is true at a last moment of time, and $ML\bot$ is true at every moment which precedes a last moment; so if time has a last moment, one disjunct or the other, and therefore the whole disjunction, is true at every moment. See also Prior (1967), p. 73.

3 More results about characterization

General characterization theorems

In the previous chapter we gave completeness proofs for a number of particular modal systems; and these proofs, together with the corresponding soundness results, established that each of the systems we dealt with is characterized by a certain class of models. It is not always necessary, however, to proceed in this piecemeal fashion, for it is possible to prove a number of general characterization theorems, each of which covers a wide range of systems in a unified way. Such theorems enable one to take any system which falls under them, and work out, from its axioms, that it is characterized by such and such a class of models. In this section we shall state and prove one such theorem, and then indicate what range of systems is covered by another, much more general one.

It will be recalled that several of the systems we discussed – for example D, T, K4 and KB – were produced by adding a single axiom to K, and that in each case the system turned out to be characterized by the class of all models in which R satisfies a certain condition. When such a situation obtains – i.e. when a system $K + \alpha$ is characterized by the class of all models in which R satisfies a certain condition – we shall sometimes say, for brevity, that the wff α itself is characterized by that condition, or that the condition *corresponds* to α.

So far we have been spelling out in words the various conditions on R that we have considered; but we can also express them in a formalized manner by formulae of the Lower (or First-order) Predicate Calculus (LPC) in which the only predicates are the two-place predicates R and =. (We have in fact occasionally done this already, as on p. 36.) Thus the reflexiveness of R is expressed by the formula

$$(\forall w)wRw,$$

its transitivity by the formula

$$(\forall w_1)(\forall w_2)(\forall w_3)((w_1Rw_2 . w_2Rw_3) \supset w_1Rw_3)$$

and so forth. The language of LPC is, of course, no part of the language of propositional modal logic; but the fact that we can use LPC to formulate conditions on R shows that one way – and in fact an illuminating way – of looking at many characterization results is as establishing a correspondence, of the kind indicated in the previous paragraph, between wff of propositional modal logic on the one hand and certain wff of (non-modal) LPC on the other.

What the general characterization theorems do is to show how to take any modal wff of a certain very general kind and 'translate' it into a wff of LPC, in such a way that the system formed by adding any number of such modal wff to K will be characterized by precisely those models which satisfy all the conditions expressed in the corresponding wff of LPC.

In stating and discussing these theorems we shall use the notation explained on p. 8, and also the term 'affirmative modality' for any unbroken sequence of Ls and/or Ms, including the 'empty' sequence which consists of no modal operators at all.

The characterization theorem that we shall now state and prove is due to Lemmon and Scott.[1] It covers all wff of the form $Ap \supset Bp$, where A and B are affirmative modalities (possibly empty), provided that in A all the Ms, if there are any, come before any of the Ls, and in B all the Ls, if there are any, come before any of the Ms. It covers, that is, all wff of the form

$$G': \quad M^mL^np \supset L^jM^kp$$

where m, n, j and k are any natural numbers, including 0. Many of the axioms we have so far used in constructing extensions of K (e.g. **T**, **4**, **B**, **E** and **G1**) have in fact been of this form.

THEOREM 3.1

Any wff of the form G′ corresponds to the following condition on R:

C: $(\forall w_1)(\forall w_2)(\forall w_3)((w_1 R^m w_2 . w_1 R^j w_3)$
   $\supset (\exists w_4)(w_2 R^n w_4 . w_3 R^k w_4))$

This condition can be visualized in this way: Whenever a pattern of the following kind occurs in a model

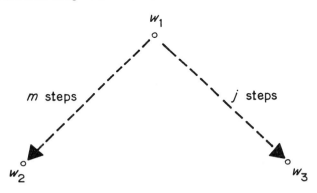

it is always continued thus:

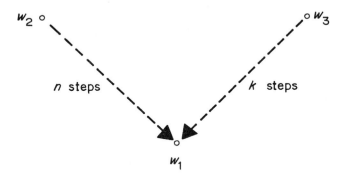

PROOF

The proof consists first of a soundness proof and then of a completeness proof.

For soundness we have to show that a wff α of the form G′ is valid in every model in which R satisfies the corresponding condition C. Suppose that any such model contains a world w_1

in which α is false. This can only be because

(i) $V(M^m L^n p, w_1) = 1$

and

(ii) $V(L^j M^k p, w_1) = 0$

By (i), there must then be some world, w_2, accessible from w_1 in m steps, such that

(iii) $V(L^n p, w_2) = 1$

and by (ii), there must be some world, w_3, accessible from w_1 in j steps, such that

(iv) $V(M^k p, w_3) = 0$

But R satisfies C; so there must also be in the model some world, w_4, which is accessible from w_2 in n steps and also from w_3 in k steps. But by (iii), p must be true in every world accessible from w_2 in n steps, and by (iv), p must be false in every world accessible from w_3 in k steps. Hence we have both $V(p, w_4) = 1$ and $V(p, w_4) = 0$, which is impossible. Thus α cannot be false in any world in any model in which R satisfies the relevant condition C.

For completeness what we have to prove is that in the canonical model for any normal modal system in which a wff of the form G' is a theorem, R satisfies the relevant condition C. The proof is a generalization of the proof given on pp. 32f. that R is convergent in the canonical model for S4.2, and the reader may find it helpful to look back at that proof.

Suppose, then, that for some $w_1, w_2, w_3 \in W$ in the canonical model for a system S in which

(1) $M^m L^n p \supset L^j M^k p$

is a theorem, we have $w_1 R^m w_2$ and $w_1 R^j w_3$. We want to show that there is also in W some w_4 such that both $w_2 R^n w_4$ and $w_3 R^k w_4$. In virtue of Theorem 2.8 (p. 26), it is sufficient for this purpose to show that

(Λ) $\{\alpha : L^n \alpha \in w_2\} \cup \{\beta : L^k \beta \in w_3\}$

is S-consistent. Now suppose it is not. This means that for some

wff $L^n\alpha \in w_2$ and some **wff** $L^k\beta \in w_3$,

$$\vdash_s \alpha \supset \sim \beta$$

From this, by repeated applications of DR3 and LMI, we have

(2) $\vdash_s M^k\alpha \supset \sim L^k\beta$

Next (again by Theorem 2.8), since $L^n\alpha \in w_2$ and $w_1 R^m w_2$, we must have $M^m L^n\alpha \in w_1$. Therefore by (1) we have $L^j M^k\alpha \in w_1$; and hence, since $w_1 R^j w_3$, we have $M^k\alpha \in w_3$. But then (2) gives us $\sim L^k\beta \in w_3$, which contradicts the assumption that $L^k\beta \in w_3$, Thus Λ is consistent, and completeness is thereby proved.

This completes the proof of Theorem 3.1.

We shall now give some illustrations of how the theorem covers some of the axioms we have already used.

(a) **G1** is of course simply the instance of G′ in which $m = n = j = k = 1$, and in this case C is just convergence as we defined it on p. 31.

(b) Consider next the axiom **T**, i.e. $Lp \supset p$. This is G′ with $n = 1$ and $m = j = k = 0$. Hence C spells out as

$$(\forall w_1)(\forall w_2)(\forall w_3)((w_1 = w_2 . w_1 = w_3)$$
$$\supset (\exists w_4)(w_2 R w_4 . w_3 = w_4))$$

This may seem a strange and cumbersome way of expressing reflexiveness, but that is precisely what it expresses nevertheless. For what it says is that if w_1, w_2 and w_3 are all the very same world, then that world is related to a w_4 which itself is just that same world again; and it is not hard to see that this is merely a long-winded way of saying that every world is related to itself.

(c) Consider now the axiom **E**, which we added to T to produce S5. It is convenient here to take **E** in the form $Mp \supset LMp$, which is G′ with $m = j = k = 1$ and $n = 0$. So C becomes

$$(\forall w_1)(\forall w_2)(\forall w_3)((w_1 R w_2 . w_1 R w_3)$$
$$\supset (\exists w_4)(w_2 = w_4 . w_3 R w_4))$$

What this means is that if any world is related to each of two worlds, then one of these two worlds is related to the other; and this is precisely the condition that characterizes the system KE. It is not, of course, equivalence; but if combined with reflexiveness (which corresponds to **T**) it yields precisely equivalence. We leave the proof of this last point to the reader.

The other theorem to which we shall refer generalizes a conjecture made by Lemmon and Scott, and has been proved by Sahlqvist.[2] The formulae covered by it are all those of the form

Sahl $L^n(\alpha \supset \beta)$

where $n \geqslant 0$ and α and β are any wff which satisfy the following conditions respectively:

α is a wff in which (i) no operators occur except L, M, $\vee$, . and $\sim$, (ii) negation signs occur only immediately before variables, and (iii) no occurrence of M, $\vee$ or . lies within the scope of any occurrence of L.

β is a wff in which no operators occur except L, M, $\vee$ and . ($\sim$ is not permitted).

This is a much wider class of wff then those covered by **G'**, but it should be clear that it covers all the latter.

Some examples of systems which are axiomatizable by instances of **Sahl** which are not instances of G' are Ver, MV and S4.3; for although the axioms we used for these systems in the previous chapter are not instances of **Sahl** as they stand, it is easy to find alternative axioms for them which are. Thus:

Ver can be axiomatized as $K + q \supset Lp$
MV can be axiomatized as $K + Mq \supset MLp$
S4.3 can be axiomatized as $S4 + M(Lp.q) \supset L(Mq \vee p)$

The condition on **R** which corresponds to **Sahl** is quite complicated, and we shall not state it here but simply refer the interested reader to Sahlqvist's paper. Our main reason for referring to the theorem is to make the point that the problem of characterizing systems by means of a condition on **R** which is expressible in LPC has been definitively solved for all systems that can be axiomatized by adding any number of wff of the form **Sahl** to K. By far the bulk of the normal modal systems discussed in the literature of the subject are in fact of this kind. Certainly all the systems we have so far mentioned in this book are.

If a modal system is characterized by some class of models that can be specified solely by a condition on **R** which is expressible in the language of LPC, then that system is said to be *first-order* *definable.* Thus any system formed by adding any number of instances of **Sahl** to K is first-order definable. There are, however, some quite simple wff which are not instances of **Sahl**. One of these, which has received a good deal of discussion, is

M $LMp \supset MLp$

The mere fact that such a wff occurs in an axiomatic basis for a system is not, of course, sufficient to show that that system is not first-order definable. Goldblatt, however, has shown that in fact K + **M** is not first-order definable, though Lemmon has shown that both S4 + **M** and K4 + **M** are.[3]

Conditions not corresponding to any axiom
We have seen that if we have a modal wff, α, which is not a theorem of K, there is often, but not always, a wff β of LPC which expresses a corresponding condition on R, in the sense that the system K + α is characterized by the class of all models in which R satisfies the condition expressed by β. But what, we may wonder, is the position about the reverse direction? Suppose, that is, that we have a wff β of LPC which expresses a (non-trivial) condition on R, and that the class of models which satisfy that condition is therefore narrower than the class of all models; is there then always some modal wff, α, not a theorem of K, such that K + α is characterized by the class of all models in which R satisfies the condition expressed by β? The answer is that here we have an analogous situation: sometimes there is such a modal wff, but sometimes there is not. We have seen several examples for which there is one, but we shall now consider some cases for which there is not.

One example is the LPC wff

$(\forall w) \sim w\mathbf{R}w$

which expresses the condition of irreflexiveness, just as

$(\forall w)w\mathbf{R}w$

expresses reflexiveness. Now we have found that the class of all reflexive models characterizes the system T, and thus that reflexiveness corresponds to the modal wff $Lp \supset p$. We can, of course, just as easily consider the class of all *irreflexive* models;

but if we enquire what system this characterizes, it turns out that the system in question is not any proper extension of K, but simply K itself. In other words, there are no modal wff that are valid in all irreflexive models, over and above those that are valid in all models whatsoever. In that sense, there is no modal wff that answers to the LPC wff $(\forall w) \sim wRw$ in the way that $Lp \supset p$ answers to $(\forall w)wRw$.

We can prove this as follows. Given any model $\langle W, R, V \rangle$, we can define another model $\langle W^*, R^*, V^* \rangle$ in the following way. W^* is formed by replacing each world w in W by a pair of worlds, w^+ and w^-. Next, in $\langle W, R, V \rangle$ some worlds may be related to themselves and others may not. We define R^* by saying that if wRw, then both $w^+R^*w^-$ and $w^-R^*w^+$; and if not wRw, then neither $w^+R^*w^-$ nor $w^-R^*w^+$; but in neither case are we to have either $w^+R^*w^+$ or $w^-R^*w^-$. In all other respects, we make R^* a copy of R, in the sense that whenever there are *distinct* worlds w_i and w_j such w_iRw_j, we let each of w_i^+ and w_i^- be R^*-related to each of w_j^+ and w_j^-. Finally, we make V^* 'reproduce' V by letting V^* give to each variable the same truth-value at *both w^+ and w^-* as V gives to it at w, for every $w \in W$.

Formally, the new model $\langle W^*, R^*, V^* \rangle$ is defined thus:

(1) $W^* = \{u : u = w^+ \text{ or } u = w^-, \text{ for each } w \in W\}$
(2) For any $u, v \in W^*$, uR^*v iff
    either   (i) $u = w^+, v = w^-$ and wRw
    or   (ii) $u = w^-, v = w^+$ and wRw
    or   (iii) $u = w_i^+$ or w_i^-, *and* $v = w_j^+$ or w_j^-, *and* $w_i \neq w_j$, *and* w_iRw_j.
(3) For any variable p and any $u \in W^*$, if either $u = w^+$ or $u = w^-$, then $V^*(p, u) = V(p, w)$.

It is then a routine though tedious task (which we omit here) to show that for every wff α and for every world in $W^* -$ i.e. for every w^+ and every $w^- - V^*(\alpha, w^+) = V^*(\alpha, w^-) = V(\alpha, w)$. It follows that every wff that is true in some world in $\langle W, R, V \rangle$ is also true in some world in $\langle W^*, R^*, V^* \rangle$. Moreover, it is clear that $\langle W^*, R^*, V^* \rangle$ is an irreflexive model, since we have taken care to ensure that in it no world is related to itself.

Since we can follow through the procedure we have just described for any model $\langle W, R, V \rangle$ whatsoever, we can in particular do so for the canonical model for K, and in that case we obtain an irreflexive model such that every wff which is true in any world in the canonical model for K is also true in some world in that irreflexive model. Every K-consistent wff, however, is true in some world in the canonical model for K. So every K-consistent wff is true in some world in some irreflexive model; and this, as we have seen, means that K is complete with respect to the class of all irreflexive models. Moreover, it is obvious that K is sound with respect to *any* class of models, and so in particular with respect to the class of all irreflexive ones.

The result we have just proved is worth stating as a theorem:

THEOREM 3.2
K is characterized by the class of all irreflexive models.

The question now arises, can we generalize our result about irreflexiveness to apply to other normal systems as well as to K? Can we, that is, say in general that if any normal system is characterized by a certain class $\mathscr{C}$ of models, it is also characterized by the class of all the irreflexive models in $\mathscr{C}$? Clearly the answer to this is No. Take T, for example. We have shown that T is characterized by the class of all reflexive models; but of course there are no irreflexive models at all in this class, and if we ask what system is characterized by the (empty) class of irreflexive reflexive models, the answer will have to be that it is not T but the inconsistent system, in which every wff is a theorem. Nevertheless there is a related result which we *can* generalize.

Let us say that a model is a *model for S* iff it is a model in which every theorem of S is valid. In the case of T, for example our soundness proof on p. 12 amounted to a proof that every reflexive model is a model for T; but being a model for T is not the same thing as being a reflexive model, for there are also models for T which are not reflexive, and even some which are irreflexive. To see this, consider the duplication of worlds we performed a few paragraphs back to produce the irreflexive model $\langle W^*, R^*, V^* \rangle$. As we noted there, this operation can be performed on any model whatsoever; and if we perform it on a reflexive model (which we know is a model for T), the result will be an irreflexive model which is also a model for T, since every wff that is valid in the original model must also be valid in the new one. Moreover, if we perform this operation on the canonical model for any normal system whatsoever, the result will always be an irreflexive model which is a model for that system. And this easily yields the general result:

THEOREM 3.3
Any normal modal system S is characterized by the class of all irreflexive models which are models for S.

This theorem gives a precise sense in which the imposition of irreflexiveness as an extra condition on R adds no new theorems to any normal modal system.

Three other conditions which do not correspond to any modal formulae are *asymmetry, antisymmetry* and *intransitivity.* Asymmetry is the conditions expressed by

$$(\forall w_1)(\forall w_2)(w_1 R w_2 \supset \sim w_2 R w_1)$$

Antisymmetry is the condition expressed by

$$(\forall w_1)(\forall w_2)((w_1 R w_2 . w_2 R w_1) \supset w_1 = w_2)$$

– in other words it is the condition that no two *distinct* worlds are related each to the other. And intransitivity is the condition expressed by

$$(\forall w_1)(\forall w_2)(\forall w_3)((w_1 R w_2 . w_2 R w_3) \supset \sim w_1 R w_3)$$

It can be shown that K is characterized by the class of all asymmetrical models, by the class of all antisymmetrical models, and by the class of all intransitive models.[4]

There is an important general moral to be drawn from all this. Clearly every class of models uniquely determines a class of modal wff, namely the class of all and only those wff that are valid in every model in that class. Furthermore, every class of wff uniquely determines a certain class of models, namely the class of all and only those models in which every wff in that class is valid. However, there is no unique class of models by which a system is *characterized.* Any normal system S is characterized by the class of all models for S; this is its largest characterizing class, and includes all the others. But S is also characterized by the class whose only member is its canonical model, and it may also

be characterized by a great many other classes as well, some of
which include its canonical model and others of which do not.
These matters will be among those taken up in later chapters.

Exercises – 3

3.1 Given Theorem 3.1,

(a) Show that $K + MLp \supset Mp$ is characterized by the class of
models in which if w is related to w', there is a world to which both
w and w' are related.

(b) Show that $K + MMLp \supset (Lp . Mp)$ is characterized by the
class of models which satisfy both of the following conditions:

(i) $(w_1 R^2 w_2 . w_1 R w_3) \supset w_2 R w_3$

(ii) $w_1 R^2 w_2 \supset (\exists w_3)(w_1 R w_3 . w_2 R w_3)$

3.2 Show that the system MV discussed on pp. 36–8 can be
axiomatized by an instance of **Sahl** but not by any instance of G′.

3.3 Prove that K4 is characterized by the class of all transitive
irreflexive models.

3.4 Prove that KB is characterized by the class of all symmetrical
irreflexive models.

Notes

1 Lemmon and Scott (1977), pp. 51ff. See also Chellas (1980), pp. 85–90
and 182–4.
2 Sahlqvist (1975), pp. 121ff. Lemmon and Scott's conjecture (1977),
p. 78, was less general in that they considered only the cases in which
$n = 0$ and α has the form

$$M^{m_1} L^{j_1} p_1 . \dots . M^{m_k} L^{j_k} p_k$$

See also Goldblatt (1975b).
3 Goldblatt (1976), Part II, pp. 40–2. That the class of *all* models for
$K + M$ is not first-order definable is proved in Goldblatt (1975a) and in
van Benthem (1975). The proof that $S4 + M$ and $K4 + M$ are first-order
definable is in Lemmon and Scott (1977), p. 75.
4 See Sahlqvist (1975), p. 127 (Corollary 12).

4 Completeness and incompleteness in modal logic

In the previous two chapters we have had a great deal to say about the completeness of various modal systems, and the pattern of our discussions has been this: we have assumed that we have, on the one hand, a certain normal modal system, S, and on the other hand an independently specified class $\mathscr{C}$ of models. We have then defined the $\mathscr{C}$-validity of a wff as its validity in every model in $\mathscr{C}$. Finally, what we have meant by the completeness of S is that every $\mathscr{C}$-valid wff is a theorem of S. This means, of course, that the question of the completeness (or for that matter the soundness) of a system cannot even be raised until a class of models has first been specified. Completeness, that is, is always completeness with respect to a certain class of models; a system may be complete with respect to one class of models but incomplete with respect to another class; and it makes no sense to speak of a system's being complete or incomplete *simpliciter*.

Is there, however, some other, though related, sense of 'complete' in which we might speak of a system's being complete in an absolute way, some sense in which we might be able to classify systems into those that are simply complete and those that are not? In this chapter we shall define such an absolute sense of completeness, and then prove, by an example, that not all normal systems are complete in this sense.

Frames and completeness

Our first approach might perhaps be this: We might decide to define the validity of a wff, not as its validity in every model in a certain independently specified class of models, but as validity in every *model for S* in the sense explained on p. 49, and then say that a system S is complete iff every valid wff in *this* sense is a theorem of S. A model for S, it may be recalled, is defined as any model in which every theorem of S is valid, i.e. is true in every world. So the present suggestion is that we should count a system S as complete if every wff that is valid in every model in which every theorem of S is valid, is a theorem of S, and incomplete if this is not so.

This will certainly give us a sense of 'complete' in which the completeness of a system is not relative to any independently specified class of models. And at first sight it may look as if it would enable us to divide systems into those that are complete and those that are not. For although, if we take a given model for S, every theorem of S is by definition valid in it, many other wff may be valid in it too; and it may appear to be a live question about S whether it is strong enough to have as theorems all the wff that are valid in all models for S (and thus to be complete), or whether it is not. However, a little reflection will show that this is not, after all, a live question about any normal modal system. For the canonical model for S is certainly one of the models for S, and by Corollary 2.5 the *only* wff that are valid in it are the theorems of S. So for any normal modal system whatsoever, the wff that are valid in *all* models for that system are bound to be precisely its theorems. In other words, the definition of completeness that we are now considering automatically makes every normal system complete, and is in that sense an empty one.

This, however, is not the only thing we might mean by 'completeness' in an absolute sense, and perhaps it is not what we *ought* to mean. Certainly, we want to tie our account of a system's completeness firmly to the notion that every valid wff is a theorem; but the account of validity that we have given is not the only possible one, or even the most important one. For in general – not only in modal logic – when we think of a formula as valid, our intuitive idea is usually that it is 'true for all values of its variables'.

Now a model, of course, specifies only one particular value-assignment to the variables out of many that we might have chosen; and our intuitive idea of validity suggests that a more important notion than that of being true in every world in a single model $\langle$ W, R, V $\rangle$ is that of being true in every world in every model which has the same W and R as this one has, no matter how V may vary. And the same idea also suggests that when we are thinking of validity with respect to a class of models, we should confine our attention to those classes that are specified by some condition on W and/or R, and in which V is allowed to vary in every possible way.

We can make this more precise as follows. Let us distinguish two parts in any model $\langle$ W, R, V $\rangle$, the $\langle$ W, R $\rangle$ part and the V part, and let us call the $\langle$ W, R $\rangle$ part a *frame*.[1] Thus a frame consists simply of a set (of 'worlds') and a dyadic relation. We then say that a model $\langle$ W, R, V $\rangle$ is *based on* the frame $\langle$ W, R $\rangle$; alternatively, we say that $\mathscr{F}$ (= $\langle$ W, R $\rangle$) is a frame, and that $\langle$ $\mathscr{F}$, V $\rangle$ is a model based on $\mathscr{F}$. We say that a wff α is *valid on a frame* $\mathscr{F}$ iff it is valid in every model based on $\mathscr{F}$ –i.e. iff V(α, w) = 1 for every $w \in$ W in every model based on $\mathscr{F}$. And if α is *not* valid in $\mathscr{F}$ – i.e. if V(α, w) = 0 for some $w \in$ W in some model based on $\mathscr{F}$, we say that α *fails on* $\mathscr{F}$. Finally, just as we said that a model is a model for a system S iff every theorem of S is valid in that model, so we shall say that $\mathscr{F}$ is a *frame for* S iff every theorem of S is valid on $\mathscr{F}$.

Our present idea is that we should think of validity, not in terms of validity on every model in a certain class, but in terms of validity in every frame in a certain class. Of course, being valid on every frame in a certain class just is being valid in every model in a certain class – but the class of models in question must then be one which is specified by a condition on W and/or R, and not in some other way.

We can now repeat, with appropriate modifications, our definitions of soundness, completeness and characterization. Suppose we have a normal system S and a class of frames $\mathscr{C}$. Then we shall say that S is sound with respect to $\mathscr{C}$ iff every theorem of S is valid on every frame in $\mathscr{C}$. (This is the same as saying that every frame in $\mathscr{C}$ is a frame for S.) We say that S is complete with respect to $\mathscr{C}$ iff every wff that is valid on every frame in $\mathscr{C}$ is a theorem of S. And we say that S is characterized by $\mathscr{C}$ iff it is both sound and complete with respect to $\mathscr{C}$, i.e. iff its theorems are precisely those wff that are valid on every frame in $\mathscr{C}$.

This, of course, gives us an account of completeness which is relativized to a given class of frames; but we can now introduce an 'absolute' sense of 'complete' by saying that S is complete iff there is *some* class of frames which characterizes it. From now on, when we use the term 'complete' without any qualifying phrase, this is always what we shall mean by it.

The characterization proofs that we gave for various systems in earlier chapters were in fact proofs of completeness in this sense. For the classes of models by which we proved these systems to be characterized were defined solely by a condition on **R**, i.e. by a condition on a *frame*. Thus in proving that T, for example, is characterized by the class of all models in which **R** is reflexive we showed that it is characterized by the class of all reflexive *frames*, and thereby of course that there is a class of frames which characterizes it. Analogous remarks apply to the other systems we discussed.

When we want to prove that a system is sound with respect to a certain class of frames, it is sufficient to show that each of its axioms is valid on every frame in that class. The reason is that validity on a frame, unlike validity in a model, is preserved by all the three transformation rules, US, MP and N. This is an easily derived corollary of Theorem 1.2 (p. 13). One consequence of this is that one method – and in fact the most generally useful method – of showing that a wff α is not a theorem of a normal system S is to find a frame on which all the axioms of S are valid but α is not.

We mentioned on pp. 50f. that a system S may be characterized by many different classes of models. Similarly, it may be characterized by many different classes of frames. The largest such class will be the class of all the frames that are frames for S, since clearly if S is characterized by any class of frames at all, it is characterized by the class of all the frames for S. A system may also be characterized by a single frame. This in itself is a somewhat trivial result, since we can always think of any class of frames (and therefore of the class of all the frames for S) as together making up a single frame in which each frame in the class is a separate part, isolated from all the others. A system may, however, be characterized by a single frame in a less trivial sense. In proving the completeness of T, for example, we showed that the *frame* of its canonical model is a reflexive frame; and from this it is easy to prove that that single frame by itself characterizes T.

At this point one might begin to wonder whether, in our present sense of 'complete', every normal modal system will be bound to be complete, as turned out to be the case for the sense of 'complete' that we toyed with on p. 53. This, however, is not so. It is certainly the case, as we have shown, that every normal modal system is characterized by the class of *models* whose only member is its canonical model; but it does not follow that it is characterized by the class of *frames* whose only member is the frame of its canonical model, or by any other class of frames, for that matter. For the canonical model for S is, after all, a *model*, not merely a frame; that is, it includes a specific value-assignment, and does not consist merely of a set of worlds and a relation defined over them. And while it is undoubtedly the case that all the theorems of S are true in every world in the canonical model for S, $\langle$ W, R, V $\rangle$, it does not follow that they would all still be true in every world in every model that we might form by keeping the same W and R but replacing V by some other value-assignment to the variables. To put this in another way, although the canonical model for S is always a model for S, this in itself does not guarantee that its frame is a frame for S.

In many cases, of course, including all the systems we have so far considered, the frame of the canonical model for S *is* a frame for S; and when this is so, we say that S is a *canonical* system.[2] It is easy to see that every system that is canonical is also complete. For with *any* system S, whether it is canonical or not, every wff that is valid on the frame of its canonical model must be valid in the canonical model itself, and hence, by Corollary 2.5, must be a theorem of S; so if, in addition, every theorem of S is valid on that frame (i.e. if S is canonical), then that frame will characterize S, and therefore S will be characterized by at least one class of frames. We cannot, however, equate being canonical with being complete; for it is conceivable that a system might be characterized by *some* class of frames, even though the frame of its canonical model was not a frame for the system. Such a system – and in fact there are systems of this kind, as we shall see in chapter 6 – would then be complete but not canonical. So the fact that a system is not canonical still leaves open the question of whether or not it is complete.

An incomplete normal modal system

Most of the incomplete modal systems that are found in the literature are very complicated.[3] Some, however, are not, and we shall discuss a quite simple one. This is due to van Benthem,[4] and we shall call it 'VB'. It is produced by adding to K the single axiom

    VB $MLp \lor L(L(Lq \supset q) \supset q)$

This axiom is reminiscent of the axiom for a system we discussed on pp. 36–8, namely the system MV, which is K +

    MV $MLp \lor Lp$

To prove that VB is an incomplete system we shall prove two things:

(A) That every frame for the system VB is also a frame for the system MV;
(B) That **MV** is not a theorem of VB.

Let us see first of all how this will demonstrate that VB is an incomplete system. Consider any class of frames each of which is a frame for VB. By (A), every frame in this class is also a frame on which the wff **MV** is valid. But by (B), **MV** is not a theorem of VB. Hence every class of frames for VB validates some non-theorem of VB, and so no class of frames whatsoever can characterize the system. To put it in another way, there can be no class of frames with respect to which VB is *both* sound *and* complete.

First, then, we shall prove (A). We do this by contraposition: i.e. we prove that if $\mathscr{F}$ is not a frame for MV, then it is not a frame for VB either. Now on p. 38 we showed that a model is a model for MV iff in it every $w \in W$ either is a dead end or can see some dead end; and since this condition is purely a condition on R, we can re-phrase this result by saying that a *frame* is a frame for MV iff in it every $w \in W$ either is a dead end or can see some dead end. Consider, then, any frame which is not of this kind; that is, any frame $\mathscr{F}$ in which there is some $w^* \in W$ which (a) can see something, and (b) is such that everything that it can see, can also see something. We shall show that in that case $\mathscr{F}$ is not a frame for VB, and we shall do so by defining a model $\langle \mathscr{F}, V \rangle$ based on $\mathscr{F}$ in which

$$MLp \lor L(L(Lq \supset q) \supset q)$$

is false in w^*. To do this, we take some world $v^* \in W$ which w^* can see (and by (a) there must be at least one such world), and we define V by letting p be false in every world in W, and letting q be false in v^* but true in every other world. (The values assigned to other variables are, of course, irrelevant.)

We now show that VB is false at w^* in this model.

(i) Take any world w such that $w^* R w$. By (b) above, w can see some world in W. But p is false in every world in W. So w can see some world at which p is false, and so $V(Lp, w) = 0$. Since this holds for every w that w^* can see, we have $V(MLp, w^*) = 0$.

(ii) Since q is true everywhere except at v^*, $Lq \supset q$ must be true everywhere, except possibly at v^* itself. So if v^* cannot see itself, $Lq \supset q$ is true in every world that it can see. But equally, if v^* *can* see itself, $Lq \supset q$ will be true in it; for then, since q is false in v^*, Lq will be false there too, and that is enough to make $Lq \supset q$ true in it. Thus in either case, $Lq \supset q$ is true in every world that v^* can see, and so $L(Lq \supset q)$ is true at v^*. However, q is false there. Therefore $L(Lq \supset q) \supset q$ is false there. As a result, since $w^* R v^*$, $L(L(Lq \supset q) \supset q)$ is false in w^*.

We thus find that, in the model we have constructed on $\mathscr{F}$, each disjunct in **VB**, and therefore **VB** itself, is false in w^*. Therefore $\mathscr{F}$ is not a frame for VB, and so (A) is proved.

We now turn to the proof of (B), i.e. that **MV** is not a theorem of the system VB. Here, however, we immediately strike a difficulty, because the usual method of proving that α is not a theorem of S – namely, finding a frame on which all the axioms of S are valid but α is not – is not available to us in the present case; for, as we have just shown, there are no frames on which **VB** is valid but **MV** is not. It would, to be sure, be easy to find a *model* in which **VB** is valid but **MV** is not, but this would not be sufficient. For, as we saw on p. 13, validity in a model is not preserved by US; so even if a wff was invalid in our chosen model, it might nevertheless still be a theorem of VB.

What van Benthem does in order to overcome this difficulty is to use a property which is in a sense intermediate between validity in a model and validity on a frame. This property is that of being valid in every one of a specified sub-class of the models based on a certain frame. The sub-class of models in question is defined in such a way that not merely the axiom **VB** itself but every substitution-instance of it is valid in every model in this sub-class. It then follows, by Theorem 1.2, that every theorem of VB is valid in every such model. But we can show that **MV** is not, and so its non-theoremhood is proved.

The frame that van Benthem uses[5] can be described as follows. The worlds in W form a set indexed by all the natural (finite) numbers, including 0, together with two 'infinite' numbers ω and $\omega + 1$. R is then defined by stipulating that if n is finite, w_n can see every world with an index less than n; that w_ω can see every world with a finite index; that $w_{\omega+1}$ can see w_ω but nothing else; and that no world can see itself. The formal definitions are:

(1) $W = \{w_0, w_1, \ldots, w_i, \ldots, w_\omega, w_{\omega+1}\}$

(2) For any w_i and $w_j \in W$, $w_i R w_j$ iff *either*
  (i) $i > j$ and $i \neq \omega + 1$ *or*
  (ii) $i = \omega + 1$ and $j = \omega$.

Let $\mathscr{F}$ be the frame $\langle W, R \rangle$ thus defined. It may be pictured like this:

$$w_{\omega+1}$$
$$\downarrow$$
$$w_0 \quad w_1 \ldots w_i \ldots w_\omega$$

We next define certain subsets of W as *allowable* sets of worlds. These are

(a) All finite subsets of W which do not contain w_ω;
and

(b) The complements of all the sets specified in (a). (Note that the empty set $\varnothing$ is allowable because it is finite and does not contain w_ω, and that W itself is allowable because it is the complement of $\varnothing$.)

We now say that V is an *allowable value-assignment* iff, for every variable p, all the worlds in which p is true form an allowable subset of W. And we say that an *allowable model* (based on $\mathscr{F}$) is any model $\langle \mathscr{F}, V \rangle$ in which V is an allowable value-assignment.

Let us call the class of all allowable models based on $\mathscr{F}$, Π. Then the property we have in mind, which we can show to be possessed by every theorem of VB but not by **MV**, is that of being *valid in every model* in Π ('Π-valid' for short).

By Theorem 1.2, in order to show that every theorem of VB is Π-valid it will be sufficient to show that every substitution-instance of the axiom **VB** is Π-valid. In the proof we shall give of this, a crucial step will be that in any model in Π, not only every variable, but every wff without restriction, has an allowable value-assignment; so we shall prove this first. Given a model $\langle W, R, V \rangle$, let us use the notation '$|\alpha|$' for the set of just those worlds in W in which α is true in that model. I.e. given $\langle W, R, V \rangle$,

$$|\alpha| = \{w \in W : V(\alpha, w) = 1\}$$

Our desired result (stated as Corollary 4.2, p. 61) will then be an immediate consequence of the following lemma:

LEMMA 4.1

In any model $\langle \mathscr{F}, V \rangle$ based on $\mathscr{F}$ as defined above, if $|p|$ is allowable for every variable p, then $|\alpha|$ is allowable for every wff α.

We sketch the proof of this lemma and leave the details to the reader. It is sufficient to prove that if $|\alpha|$ and $|\beta|$ are allowable, so are $|\sim \alpha|$, $|\alpha \vee \beta|$ and $|L\alpha|$, since all wff are built up from variables by $\sim$, $\vee$ and L. Now by $[V \sim]$, $|\sim \alpha|$ is the complement of $|\alpha|$, and our definition of allowable sets ensures that if any set is allowable, so is its complement. Next, by $[V \vee]$, $|\alpha \vee \beta|$ is the union of $|\alpha|$ and $|\beta|$, and it is not difficult to check that if each of $|\alpha|$ and $|\beta|$ is allowable, so is their union. Finally, consider $|L\alpha|$. We can in fact show that $|L\alpha|$ is allowable for any wff α, no matter whether $|\alpha|$ itself is allowable or not. For *any* value-assignment must either (i) make α false at w_n for some finite n, or else (ii) make α true at w_n for every finite n. Now case (i) makes $L\alpha$ false at every world indexed by a natural number greater than n, and also at w_ω; so the only worlds at which $L\alpha$ can be true are some of those below w_n, together, possibly, with w_n itself and $w_{\omega+1}$, and clearly such worlds form a set which is finite and does not contain w_ω, and is therefore allowable. And in case (ii), $L\alpha$ must be true everywhere except perhaps at $w_{\omega+1}$; so then $|L\alpha|$ is the complement either of the empty set of worlds or else of $\{w_{\omega+1}\}$, and hence is again allowable.

This completes our sketch of the proof of Lemma 4.1. We therefore immediately have our desired result, viz.

COROLLARY 4.2
In every model in Π, $|\alpha|$ is an allowable subset of W, for every wff α.

We are now ready to tackle directly the proofs that every theorem of VB is Π-valid but that **MV** is not.

We shall prove the latter first. Let $\langle \mathscr{F}, V \rangle$ be a model based on $\mathscr{F}$ in which p is false in every $w \in W$. This model is clearly in Π, since $\varnothing$ is an allowable subset of W. (The variables other than p are irrelevant, and so can be given any allowable value-assignment we choose.) Then clearly Lp is false in w_ω; and since this is the only world that $w_{\omega+1}$ can see, MLp is false in $w_{\omega+1}$. Moreover, since p is false in w_ω, Lp is false in $w_{\omega+1}$. Hence each disjunct in **MV**, and therefore **MV** itself, is false in $w_{\omega+1}$ in this model; so **MV** is not Π-valid.

The other thing we have to prove is that every theorem of VB is Π-valid. As we have already noted, Theorem 1.2 shows that it is sufficient for this purpose to show that every substitution-instance of the axiom **VB** is Π-valid. What this means is that, for any arbitrary wff α and β,

VB': $\quad ML\alpha \vee L(L(L\beta \supset \beta) \supset \beta)$

is true in every world in any model based on $\mathscr{F}$ in which all the variables have allowable value-assignments. By Corollary 4.2, α and β will also have allowable value-assignments in any such model.

Now w_0 is a dead end; so every wff of the form $L\gamma$, and in particular $L(L(L\beta \supset \beta) \supset \beta)$, is true in w_0, and therefore so is **VB'**.

Next, every world except w_0 and $w_{\omega+1}$ can see a dead end (viz. w_0). So, since $L\alpha$ must be true in any dead end, $ML\alpha$ is true in all these worlds, and therefore so once more is **VB′**.

All that remains, therefore is to show that **VB′** is true in $w_{\omega+1}$ in every model in Π. We do this by proving that if **VB′** is false in $w_{\omega+1}$ in any model based on $\mathscr{F}$, then β must have a non-allowable value-assignment in that model; for then, by Corollary 4.2, the model cannot be in Π. Suppose, then, that **VB′** is false in $w_{\omega+1}$. Then its second disjunct, $L(L(L\beta \supset \beta) \supset \beta)$, must be false there. But the only world that $w_{\omega+1}$ can see is w_ω; therefore $L(L\beta \supset \beta) \supset \beta$ must be false in w_ω, which means that

(i) β is false in w_ω

and

(ii) $L(L\beta \supset \beta)$ is true in w_ω.

Now w_ω can see every w_n where n is a natural number. Therefore (ii) gives us

(iii) $L\beta \supset \beta$ is true in w_n, for every natural number n.

Now consider w_0. This is a dead end, so $L\beta$ is true in it. Hence by (iii), so is β. Now consider any w_n where n is a natural number > 0, and suppose that β is true in every w_m where $m < n$. This will make $L\beta$ true at w_n, and hence, by (iii) again, β will be true at w_n. As a result, β is true at every w_n, where n is a natural number, and there are infinitely many of these. But by (i), β is not true at w_ω. Thus $|\beta|$ is an infinite set which does not contain w_ω; and this set is not an allowable one, which is what we set out to prove.

We have therefore shown that every theorem of VB is Π-valid but that **MV** is not. This establishes (B) on p. 57, namely that **MV** is not a theorem of VB, and thereby completes the proof that VB is an incomplete system.

General frames

In the proof we have just given, we have spoken on the one hand of a frame, defined in the usual way as a set of worlds and a relation, and on the other hand of a certain limited class of models based on that frame. There is, however, another way in which we could look at this. Instead of thinking of ourselves as starting from a structure consisting only of a set W and a relation R, we could think of ourselves as starting from a structure consisting of these together with a set P of 'allowable' sets of members of W; and we could then think of a model as being derived from such a structure by adding to it any value-assignment to the variables which satisfies the condition that, for every variable p, $|p|$ is one of the sets in P. Such a structure $\langle W, R, P \rangle$, though not a frame in the sense in which we have been using the term 'frame', would be better described as a frame than as a model, since it would contain no value-assignment and therefore would not determine the values of wff in various worlds. In order to ensure that $\langle W, R, P \rangle$ could yield the sort of proof we gave in the previous section, however, we should have to require that P should be so selected that once we were given that $|p| \in P$ for every variable p, we could be sure that $|\alpha| \in P$ for every wff α. To achieve this, we have to require that P should be so chosen that whenever any set of worlds, A, is in P, then so is its complement (for the sake of the induction on $\sim$), that whenever A and B are both in P, then so is their union (for the sake of the induction on $\vee$), and that whenever A is in P, so is the set of all worlds that can see *only* members of A (for the sake of the induction on L). A structure $\langle W, R, P \rangle$ in which P satisfies these conditions is called a *general frame* by van Benthem.[6] The formal definition is this:

$\langle W, R, P \rangle$ is a *general frame* iff

(a) W is a non-empty set;
(b) R is a dyadic relation defined over W;
(c) P is a set of sets of members of W (i.e. $P \subseteq \mathscr{P}W$) satisfying the following conditions:
  (i) If $A \in P$, then $W - A \in P$,
  (ii) If $A \in P$ and $B \in P$, then $A \cup B \in P$, and
  (iii) If $A \in P$, then $\{w \in W : (\forall w' \in W)(wRw' \supset w' \in A)\} \in P$.

A model based on a general frame $\langle W, R, P \rangle$ will then be any structure $\langle W, R, P, V \rangle$, where V is a value-assignment to the variables which makes $|p| \in P$ for every variable p. The standard rules $[V \sim]$, $[V \vee]$ and $[VL]$ are assumed to hold. We shall then say, by a natural extension of our earlier definitions, that a wff is valid on a given general frame iff it is valid in (true in every world in) every model based on that general frame; that a general frame is a general frame for a system S iff every theorem of S is valid on that general frame; and that S is characterized by a class $\mathscr{C}$ of general frames iff, for every wff α, α is a theorem of S iff α is valid on every (general) frame in $\mathscr{C}$.

Now suppose we consider the frame $\langle W, R \rangle$ of the canonical model for any normal modal system S, and suppose we define the set P of allowable sets of worlds by saying that A is an allowable set iff there is some wff α which is true in that canonical model in every world in A but in no other world. (I.e. $P = \{A \subseteq W : \exists \alpha (A = |\alpha|)\}$.) Then it is not hard to show that $\langle W, R, P \rangle$, as so defined, is a general frame which characterizes S. And this has the consequence that *every* normal modal system is characterized by the class of all the general frames for that system. Thus if we were to suggest, as a third possible account of the completeness of a system in some absolute sense, that a system should be said to be complete iff it is characterized by some class of *general* frames, then this – like the first account which we considered and dismissed on p. 53, but unlike the second one which we considered and adopted on pp. 54f. – would have the consequence that every normal modal system is complete.

General frames are like models in that each normal modal system is characterized by some class of them, and indeed each is characterized by a single one. But general frames are unlike models in that if any wff is valid on a general frame, so are all its substitution-instances. Ordinary frames (which are sometimes called *Kripke frames* in contexts in which it is important to distinguish them from general frames) of course also have this property; but many models do not, as we observed on p. 13. It is this last-mentioned fact which suggests that an intuitively satisfactory account of validity for a modal system should be in terms of frames, of one kind or another, rather than in terms of models. Of the two kinds of frames we have discussed, Kripke frames, unlike general frames, lead to an account of completeness which yields a real distinction between systems which are complete and ones which are not; but general frames sometimes enable us to construct independence proofs where neither Kripke frames nor models would be of service.

What might we understand by incompleteness?

The incomplete system VB which we have discussed in this chapter is certainly one which has a very simple axiomatic basis, but it is difficult to get an intuitive grasp of just *how* it is incomplete – that is, of how it can be that the system cannot precisely match any condition on a frame and yet can match such a condition if it is combined with a restriction on the permitted value-assignments. (This, indeed, seems also to be true of the other incomplete systems that have been described in the literature.) We may, however, be helped in this matter by comparing VB with an incomplete system of *tense* logic which has been produced by S.K. Thomason.[7] Tense logic lies outside the scope of this book, since it contains two 'necessity' operators, one for the past and one for the future; nevertheless it seems worthwhile to mention Thomason's system here, since it seems possible to get an intuitive 'feel' for the source of its incompleteness. One of the consequences of Thomason's axioms, given the interpretation he intends them to have, is that time never comes to an end. Another of their consequences is that every proposition eventually takes on an unvarying truth-value (though, since time is never-ending, there need be no specific moment after which *all* propositions have unvarying truth-values). Thomason is able to prove that there are no Kripke frames at all for his system and hence, of course, it is not characterized by any class of frames; and we may well feel, intuitively, that this is not a surprising result, for this reason: if we give the elements in a frame a temporal interpretation (e.g. by taking the 'worlds' as moments of time and R as the relation *is earlier than*), then a frame, or a class of frames, can be thought of as expressing a possible structure for time; but it is very hard to see how the mere structure of (non-ending) time could by itself be sufficient to ensure that every proposition will eventually have a constant truth-value. It is, however, not difficult in principle to conceive that the structure of time *together with some restriction on permitted value-assignments* might have just such an effect. The analogy with the semantics for VB is this: our definition of the class Π of allowable models has the effect of ensuring that, for any wff α, either α itself or $\sim \alpha$ will be true at only a finite number of the w_ns; and this means that for every wff there is some α_n after which it retains an unvarying truth-value which it still keeps at w_ω (though not necessarily at $w_{\omega+1}$). It again seems intuitively reasonable (as it did with Thomason's system) to expect that a system characterized by such a class of models would not be determined solely by a condition on a Kripke frame, but only by this in conjunction with a restriction on value-assignments.

Exercises – 4

4.1 Prove that K together with the following axioms is not complete:

    (i) $LMq \supset L(Lp \supset p)$
    (ii) $L(L(Lp \supset p) \supset Lp)$

4.2 (a) Prove that **VB** is a theorem of the system MV.

    (b) Prove that MV is precisely the system characterized by the class of all frames for **VB**.

4.3 Given that $Lp \supset LLp$ is not a theorem of the system $K + L(p \equiv Lp) \supset Lp$, prove that this system is not complete. (See Boolos (1980), p. 17.)

4.4 Set out fully the proof that every normal modal system is characterized by a class of general frames.

Notes

1 The word 'frame' in this sense seems to have been first used in print in Segerberg (1968b), but Segerberg has informed us privately that the word was suggested to him by Dana Scott. Lemmon and Scott (1977) called frames 'world systems'. Kripke used the term 'model structure' in a related but not quite identical sense (see *IML*, pp. 350f.).

2 The use of 'canonical' in this sense is due to Fine (1975a). Segerberg (1971), p. 29, calls such systems *natural*. Fine has, however, a different use for the term 'natural system'. He defines a *natural model* as one in which (i) for every $w \neq w'$ there is some wff α such that $V(\alpha, w) \neq V(\alpha, w')$, and (ii) if not wRw', then there is a wff α such that $V(L\alpha, w) = 1$ and $V(\alpha, w') = 0$. He then calls a system S a *natural system* iff not only the frame of its canonical model but the frame of *every* natural model for S is a frame for S. It should be clear that every system that is natural in this sense is canonical, but Fine proves that $S4 + LMp \supset MLp$ (see p. 47 above) is canonical but not (in his sense) natural.

    Another result which Fine establishes in the same paper is that every system which is first-order definable, in the sense explained on pp. 46f. above, is canonical. Note, however, that Fine's own sense of the term 'first-order definable', and therefore the way in which he himself expresses his result, is not the same as ours. In our sense, every first-order definable system is automatically complete. In Fine's sense, a system S is first-order definable iff the class of all the frames for S is first-order definable, and in that sense the first-order definability of a system does not guarantee its completeness. Fine therefore states his result by saying that every *complete* system which is first-order definable is canonical. In Fine's sense, though not in ours, the system VB, which we shall discuss shortly, is first-order definable; for, as we shall see, the class of all the frames for it is the same as the class of all the frames for the system MV, and that class is first-order definable (see pp. 36–8). We shall show, however, that VB is not *characterized by* that (or any other) class of frames; and it is therefore not canonical, for the reason given in the text.

3 See, e.g., Fine (1974b), S.K. Thomason (1974), van Benthem (1978), (1979b) and Boolos (1980). Blok (1980) proves that there are $2^{\aleph_0}$ incomplete systems, but does not give any examples. Fine (op. cit., p. 28) notes that a method which he uses in Fine (1974c) will produce $2^{\aleph_0}$ incomplete extensions of S4.

4 Van Benthem (1979b). Our axiom is a variant of his.

5 Van Benthem (1979b), p. 73. Van Benthem's own frame is in fact slightly different from the one we describe, since it allows $w_\omega R w_\omega$; but this difference does not affect the proof of incompleteness. The system characterized by the class Π of models is actually stronger than VB, but it can be finitely axiomatized; see Cresswell (1984).

6 Van Benthem (1978). (The term 'general', as used here, is derived from its much earlier use by Leon Henkin in connection with an analogous situation in higher order predicate logic.) Makinson (1970) calls such structures *relational frames*, and S.K. Thomason (1972a, p. 151), calls them *first-order structures*. Thomason (op. cit., p. 154) then imposes two extra conditions on such structures to obtain what he calls *refined structures*. These conditions are (a) that if $w \neq w'$, then there is an allowable set A such that $w \in A$ but $w' \notin A$; and (b) that if not wRw', then there is an allowable set A such that $w \in A$ but $w' \notin A$. (Thomason's refined structures link with Fine's natural models – see note 2, above). Goldblatt (1976), Part I, p. 64, imposes still further conditions to obtain what he calls *descriptive frames*. (Descriptive frames link with canonical models.)

7 S.K. Thomason (1972a), pp. 153f.

5 Frames and models

In the previous chapter we introduced the distinction between a model and the frame on which it is based. We also distinguished between ordinary (or Kripke) frames and general frames, but we shall not discuss general frames any further and from now on 'frame' will always mean simply a Kripke frame, i.e. a pair $\langle W, R \rangle$.

We already know that many modal systems are characterized by classes of frames, and in particular by conditions on R; but there is much more that we can learn about frames, and their relation to modal systems, than that, as we shall see in this chapter and later ones. The main theme of the present chapter will be certain ways in which one model or frame, or one class of models or class of frames, can, for certain purposes, be made to do the work of another. The results we shall obtain will give us techniques for proving, in many cases, that a system which is characterized by a certain class of frames is also characterized by another class. We shall then illustrate the use of some of these techniques by proving that the system S4.3, which we already know to be characterized by the class of all reflexive, transitive and connected frames, is also characterized by the class of all linear frames.

Equivalent models and equivalent frames

In the proof of Theorem 3.2 on pp. 48f. a key step consisted in showing how, given a certain model, we could construct another model, of a certain desired kind, in such a way that any formula which is true in some world in one of these models is also true in some world in the other; or – what comes to the same thing – in such a way that any formula which is valid (true in every world) in one of these models is also valid in the other. When two models are related in this way, we say that they are *equivalent* models. The formal definition is this:

Two models $\langle W, R, V \rangle$ and $\langle W^*, R^*, V^* \rangle$ are *equivalent* iff, for every wff α, α is valid in $\langle W, R, V \rangle$ iff α is valid in $\langle W^*, R^*, V^* \rangle$.

We can give an analogous definition of equivalent *frames*:

Two frames $\mathcal{F}$ and $\mathcal{F}^*$ are *equivalent* iff, for every wff α, α is valid on $\mathcal{F}$ iff α is valid on $\mathcal{F}^*$.

Thus equivalent models, or equivalent frames, are simply models or frames which validate precisely the same formulae. This does not mean that they have the same structure. To take a simple example, the frame $\langle W, R \rangle$ in which $W = \{w_1, w_2\}$ and R is the empty relation, validates precisely the theorems of the Verum system, and so does the frame $\langle W^*, R^* \rangle$ in which $W^* = \{w_1\}$ and R is the empty relation. Clearly these two frames do not have the same structure, yet they are equivalent in the sense we have defined.

When two models or frames do have the same structure, they are said to be *isomorphic*. In order to express this more precisely, we first explain some terminology. Given two sets, A and A*, f is said to be a *function* from A to A* if it associates with each element x in A a unique element y in A*. The element x is then said to be *mapped* on to y by f, and y is referred to as $f(x)$. In general, f may map many distinct elements in A on to the same element, y, in A*, and we refer to the set of all such elements in A as $f^*(y)$. Expressed more formally,

$$f^*(y) = \{x \in A : f(x) = y\}$$

If, however, f maps each element in A on to a distinct element in A*, then f is said to be a 1–1 *function* (from A to A*). Next, there may or may not be some elements in A* which have no elements in A mapped on to them at all; but when there are no such elements – i.e. when every element in A* is $f(x)$ for at least one x in A – then f is said to be a function from A *onto* A*. Clearly, when f is such a function, A* can have no more members than A has. Finally, there is the special case in which f is both a 1–1 function and a function from A onto A*. In that case, it is easy to see that there is also a 1–1 function from A* onto A, and that to each element in A there corresponds a distinct element in A* and vice versa.

We can now define what it is for two models or frames to be isomorphic. In the case of frames, $\langle W, R \rangle$ and $\langle W^*, R^* \rangle$ are said to be isomorphic iff there is a 1–1 function from W onto W* such that for any w and $w' \in W$, wRw' iff $f(w)R^*f(w')$. And in the case of models, $\langle W, R, V \rangle$ and $\langle W^*, R^*, V^* \rangle$ are said to be isomorphic iff $\langle W, R \rangle$ and $\langle W^*, R^* \rangle$ are isomorphic frames, and in addition, for any variable p and any $w \in W$, $V(p, w) = V^*(p, f(w))$. When two frames or models are isomorphic, the function f in question is called an *isomorphism* from one frame or model to the other.

This makes precise the sense we have in mind when we say that two models or frames have the same structure. Although, as we have observed, it is possible to have equivalent frames (or models) which are not isomorphic, it should be intuitively obvious that all isomorphic frames (or models) are equivalent. In any case, this fact is an easy consequence of the theorems to be proved in the next section.

Pseudo-epimorphisms

In the definition of isomorphism the function from one model or frame to another was required to be structure-preserving in a very strict sense. There is, however, a weaker condition on a function which gives what Segerberg calls a *pseudo-epimorphism* (or for short, a *p-morphism*)[1] from one model or frame to another. An isomorphism turns out to be simply a special kind of p-morphism.

We shall now define p-morphisms and prove some theorems which relate them to equivalence.

For frames, the definition is this:

Where $\langle W, R \rangle$ and $\langle W^*, R^* \rangle$ are frames, f is a *p-morphism* from $\langle W, R \rangle$ to $\langle W^*, R^* \rangle$ iff

   (i) f is a function from W onto W* (but not necessarily a 1–1 function);

   (ii) for any w and $w' \in W$, if wRw' *then* $f(w)R^*f(w')$; and

(iii) for any u and $v \in W^*$, if uR^*v then for every $w \in f^*(u)$ there is some $w' \in f^*(v)$ such that wRw' (i.e. every world mapped on to u can see at least one of the worlds mapped on to v).

$\langle W^*, R^* \rangle$ is then said to be a p-morphic *image* of $\langle W, R \rangle$.

There are several points to notice about this definition. One is that there is nothing in it to prevent W^* from being a subset of W, or even identical with W. Another is that W^* must have no more members than W, since otherwise f could not be a function *onto* W^*. A third is that if f is not merely onto W^* but a 1–1 function onto W^*, then the p-morphism is in fact an isomorphism. A fourth point is this: given a frame $\langle W, R \rangle$ and a set W^* which is no larger than W, there will always exist a function f (in general, many such functions) from W onto W^*. For any such f, we can then always find an R^* which satisfies condition (ii), or one which satisfies condition (iii). But there is no general guarantee that there will be an R^* which will satisfy both of these conditions: this will be possible only when for every pair of worlds u and v in W^*, either each world mapped on to u can see some world mapped on to v, or else none of them can. If f does not satisfy this condition, it cannot yield us any p-morphic image of $\langle W, R \rangle$ at all.

For models, the definition is this:

Where $\langle W, R, V \rangle$ and $\langle W^*, R^*, V^* \rangle$ are models, f is a p-morphism from $\langle W, R, V \rangle$ to $\langle W^*, R^*, V^* \rangle$ iff f is a p-morphism from $\langle W, R \rangle$ to $\langle W^*, R^* \rangle$, and in addition, for every variable p and every $w \in W$, $V(p, w) = V^*(p, f(w))$.

$\langle W^*, R^*, V^* \rangle$ is then said to be a p-morphic image of $\langle W, R, V \rangle$.

Note that even if a frame $\langle W^*, R^* \rangle$ is a p-morphic image of a frame $\langle W, R \rangle$, it does not follow that there is any model based on $\langle W^*, R^* \rangle$ which is a p-morphic image of a given model $\langle W, R, V \rangle$ based on $\langle W, R \rangle$. There is such an image iff, for every $u \in W^*$, all the worlds in W which are mapped on to u coincide in the values assigned to the variables; i.e. iff, where $u \in W^*$ and w and $w' \in f^*(u)$, then $V(p, w) = V(p, w')$ for every variable p.

Our first theorem concerns models, not frames, and is to the effect that if one model is a p-morphic image of another, then the two models are equivalent.

THEOREM 5.1
Suppose that there is a p-morphism f from a model $\langle W, R, V \rangle$ to a model $\langle W^*, R^*, V^* \rangle$. Then for any wff α and any $w \in W$, $V(\alpha, w) = V^*(\alpha, f(w))$.

PROOF

The proof is by induction on the construction of a wff. If α is a variable, the theorem holds by the definition of a p-morphism. It is therefore sufficient to prove (i) that if the theorem holds for a wff β, it also holds for $\sim \beta$, (ii) that if it holds for β and for γ, it also holds for $\beta \lor \gamma$, and (iii) that if it holds for β, it also holds for $L\beta$.

(i) We take as our induction hypothesis that $V(\beta, w) = V^*(\beta, f(w))$. Now by $[V \sim]$, $V(\sim \beta, w) = 1$ iff $V(\beta, w) = 0$. By the induction hypothesis, $V(\beta, w) = 0$ iff $V^*(\beta, f(w)) = 0$. And by $[V \sim]$ again, $V^*(\beta, f(w)) = 0$ iff $V^*(\sim \beta, f(w)) = 1$. This suffices to prove (i).

(ii) We take as our inductive hypothesis that $V(\beta, w) = V^*(\beta, f(w))$ and $V(\gamma, w) = V^*(\gamma, f(w))$. Now by $[V \lor]$, $V(\beta \lor \gamma, w) = 1$ iff either $V(\beta, w) = 1$ or $V(\gamma, w) = 1$. By the induction hypothesis, the latter is the case iff either $V^*(\beta, f(w)) = 1$ or $V^*(\gamma, f(w)) = 1$. And by $[V \lor]$ again, this is so iff $V^*(\beta \lor \gamma, f(w)) = 1$. This suffices to prove (ii).

(iii) The induction for L is more complicated, and makes use of the special properties of f, which did not enter into the proofs of (i) and (ii). We take as our hypothesis that $V(\beta, w) = V^*(\beta, f(w))$, for every $w \in W$, and prove two things: (a) that if $V(L\beta, w) = 0$ then $V^*(L\beta, f(w)) = 0$, and (b) that if $V^*(L\beta, f(w)) = 0$ then $V(L\beta, w) = 0$.

(a) Suppose that $V(L\beta, w) = 0$. Then by $[VL]$ there is some $w' \in W$ such that wRw' and $V(\beta, w') = 0$. Hence by condition (ii) in the definition of a p-morphism, $f(w)R^*f(w')$. But by the induction hypothesis we have $V^*(\beta, f(w')) = 0$. So by $[VL]$, $V^*(L\beta, f(w)) = 0$.

(b) Suppose that $V^*(L\beta, f(w)) = 0$. Then by $[VL]$ there is some $u \in W^*$ such that $f(w)R^*u$ and $V^*(\beta, u) = 0$. Hence by condition (iii) in the definition of a p-morphism, there is some $w' \in W$ such that wRw' and $f(w') = u$. But by the induction hypothesis, $V(\beta, w') = V^*(\beta, f(w'))$; so, since $f(w') = u$, we have $V(\beta, w') = 0$. Thus by $[VL]$, $V(L\beta, w) = 0$.

This completes the proof of Theorem 5.1.

COROLLARY 5.2

If a model $\langle W^*, R^*, V^* \rangle$ is a p-morphic image of a model $\langle W, R, V \rangle$, then the two models are equivalent.

We now turn to consider frames. For a reason which will appear shortly, we do not have for frames a result as strong as Corollary 5.2 gives us for models. We do, however, have the following weaker, but still important, result:

THEOREM 5.3

Suppose that $\langle W^*, R^* \rangle$ is a p-morphic image of $\langle W, R \rangle$. Then for any wff α, if α is valid on $\langle W, R \rangle$, α is also valid on $\langle W^*, R^* \rangle$.

PROOF

We prove the theorem by contraposition: we assume that a wff is not valid on $\langle W^*, R^* \rangle$ and show that in that case it is not valid on $\langle W, R \rangle$. Since α is not valid on $\langle W^*, R^* \rangle$, there is a model $\langle W^*, R^*, V^* \rangle$ in which α is not valid. Let f be the p-morphism from $\langle W, R \rangle$ to $\langle W^*, R^* \rangle$. We now define the model $\langle W, R, V \rangle$, based on $\langle W, R \rangle$, in which for any variable p and any $w \in W$, $V(p, w) = V^*(p, f(w))$. Clearly $\langle W^*, R^*, V^* \rangle$ is a p-morphic image of $\langle W, R, V \rangle$. So by Corollary 5.2, α is not valid in $\langle W, R, V \rangle$, and therefore not valid on $\langle W, R \rangle$.

This proves the theorem.

It is worth while seeing clearly why we cannot have an analogue of Corollary 5.2 for frames, i.e. why the fact that $\langle W^*, R^* \rangle$ is a p-morphic image of $\langle W, R \rangle$ does not guarantee that the two frames are equivalent. It does guarantee, as we have just proved, that every wff that is valid on $\langle W, R \rangle$ is also valid on $\langle W^*, R^* \rangle$, but it does not guarantee that every wff that is valid on the latter is also valid on the former. For consider a model $\langle W^*, R^*, V^* \rangle$, based on $\langle W^*, R^* \rangle$, in which a wff α is valid. We can indeed then define a model $\langle W, R, V \rangle$, based on $\langle W, R \rangle$, by letting every variable have the same value in all the worlds in W which are mapped on to any given $u \in W^*$ as they do in u itself. This model will then have $\langle W^*, R^*, V^* \rangle$ as its p-morphic image, and we can therefore be sure that α is valid in it too. But clearly we can also have other models based on $\langle W, R \rangle$, in which V does not satisfy this condition, and α may well turn out to be invalid in many of these. So the fact that a wff is valid in every model based on $\langle W^*, R^* \rangle$ leaves open the possibility that it might be invalid in some models based on $\langle W, R \rangle$. Here is a simple example to illustrate this. Let $\langle W, R \rangle$ be the frame in which $W = \{w_1, w_2\}$ and in which $w_1 R w_2$ and $w_2 R w_2$; and let $\langle W^*, R^* \rangle$ be the frame in which $W = \{w_1\}$ and $w_1 R w_1$. Then if we let both $f(w_1)$ and $f(w_2)$ be w_1, f is a p-morphism from $\langle W, R \rangle$ to $\langle W^*, R^* \rangle$. But these frames are not equivalent, since the wff $p \supset Lp$ is valid on $\langle W^*, R^* \rangle$ but not on $\langle W, R \rangle$. The reason it is not valid on $\langle W, R \rangle$ is that it is false at w_1 in the model based on this frame in which $V(p, w_1) = 1$ and $V(p, w_2) = 0$. This is, of course, a model in which it is not the case that p has the same value in all the worlds mapped on to the same world in W^*; and as we remarked on p. 71, such a model has no p-morphic image based on $\langle W^*, R^* \rangle$.

A frame is therefore not necessarily equivalent to all of its p-morphic images. We do, however, have the following weaker result, which follows directly from Theorem 5.3.

COROLLARY 5.4
If two frames are each a p-morphic image of the other, they are equivalent.

As we noted earlier, an isomorphism is a special case of a p-morphism; and it should also be clear that if two frames are isomorphic then there is a p-morphism both from the first to the second and also from the second to the first. So the result we mentioned on p. 70, that isomorphic frames are equivalent, follows immediately from Corollary 5.4.

One example of the use of p-morphisms has in fact already occurred in an earlier chapter, though not under that name. This is the proof we gave in chapter 3 that every model is equivalent to some irreflexive model, and it may be helpful to survey that proof briefly with our recent results in mind. The essence of the proof lies in the fact that there is a p-morphism from the model $\langle W^*, R^*, V^* \rangle$ defined on p. 48, back to the original model $\langle W, R, V \rangle$. The p-morphism in this case is the function f such that, for every w^+ and $w^- \in W^*$, $f(w^+) = w$ and $f(w^-) = w$. That f is a p-morphism can be seen as follows:

Obviously f is a function from W^* onto W. Now let u and v be any worlds in W^*. Then it is clear from the definition of R^* that if uR^*v then $f(u)Rf(v)$. Thus condition (ii) in the definition of a p-morphism is satisfied.

Next, consider any w_1 and $w_2 \in W$ such that $w_1 R w_2$. The only members of $f^*(w_1)$ will be w_1^+ and w_1^-; and by the definition of R^*, we have both $w_1^+ R^* w_2^+$ and $w_1^- R^* w_2^+$. So since $w_2^+ \in f^*(w_2)$, each member of $f^*(w_1)$ is related by R^* to some member of $f^*(w_2)$. Thus condition (iii) in the definition of a p-morphism is satisfied.

Finally, V^* was so defined that for every variable p and every $w \in W^*$, $V^*(p, w) = V(p, f(w))$, so the additional condition for the p-morphism of models is also satisfied.

$\langle W, R, V \rangle$ is therefore a p-morphic image of $\langle W^*, R^*, V^* \rangle$, and so by Corollary 5.2 the two models are equivalent.

Later in this chapter (pp. 84–6) we shall give another example of the use of p-morphisms.

Distinguishable models

Theorem 5.1 states one sufficient condition for a given model's being equivalent to another one. In this section we shall be concerned with another such condition, which is in certain respects more relaxed, but in other compensating ways more stringent, than the previous one.

Among the models to which we have paid particular attention are canonical models. These models have a number of important features, one of which is that they never contain two distinct worlds, w and w', such that for every wff α, $V(\alpha, w) = V(\alpha, w')$. To put this another way: for any two worlds in a canonical model, there is always some wff which distinguishes them by being true in one but false in the other. This is, of course, a feature which is possessed by many other models as well as by canonical ones. Any model which possesses it we shall call a *distinguishable* model.[2] The formal definition is this:

A model $\langle W, R, V \rangle$ is a *distinguishable* model iff for any w and $w' \in W$ such that $w \neq w'$, there is a wff α such that $V(\alpha, w) \neq V(\alpha, w')$.

Next, given any model $\langle W, R, V \rangle$, we shall say that two worlds, w and w', in W are *equivalent worlds* (in $\langle W, R, V \rangle$) iff every wff has the same truth-value in each as it has in the other; i.e. iff for every wff α, $V(\alpha, w) = V(\alpha, w')$. We write '$w \approx w'$' to mean that w and w' are equivalent ($\approx$ is, of course, relative to some particular model). We shall call the class of all worlds in

W which are equivalent to a given $w \in W$, the *equivalence class* of w, and use the notation '$[w]$' for it. To express this formally, $[w]$ is $\{ w' \in W : w' \approx w \}$. Thus in every model, W is exhaustively partitioned into a number of equivalence classes. A *distinguishable* model, then, is one in which no two distinct worlds are equivalent; or in other words, in which each equivalence class has only one member.

It should be clear that not every model is a distinguishable one. For instance, the irreflexive models described in chapter 3 and referred to in the previous section are not distinguishable. Every model, however, is equivalent, in the sense defined above, to some distinguishable model, and in fact to a distinguishable model which contains no more worlds than it does. It is the main purpose of the present section to prove this.

THEOREM 5.5
Let $\langle W, R, V \rangle$ be any model. Then there is a distinguishable model $\langle W^*, R^*, V^* \rangle$ which is equivalent to $\langle W, R, V \rangle$ and in which W^* contains no more worlds than W does.

PROOF
The idea behind the proof is quite simple, and consists basically in 'identifying', or treating as a single world, all the worlds in each equivalence class in W.

Given $\langle W, R, V \rangle$, we define a model $\langle W^*, R^*, V^* \rangle$ as follows:

(1) W^* is a subset of W formed by taking exactly one member of each equivalence class in W.[3]

(2) R^* is defined thus: for any u and $v \in W^*$, uR^*v iff there is some w in $[v]$ such that uRw. In other words, u is to be related to v in the new model iff it is related in the original model to a world equivalent to v.

(3) V^* is simply the restriction of V to those members of W which are members of W^*. I.e. for every variable p and every $w \in W^*$, $V^*(p, w) = V(p, w)$.

We now prove that

(A)   For any wff α and any $w \in W^*$, $V^*(\alpha, w) = V(\alpha, w)$.

The proof of this is by induction on the construction of a wff. We first note that if α is a variable, (A) holds by the definition of V^*. We then have to prove (i) that if (A) holds for a wff α, it also holds for $\sim \alpha$; (ii) that if it holds for each of a pair of wff α and β, it also holds for $\alpha \vee \beta$; and (iii) that if it holds for a wff α, it also holds for $L\alpha$. This will show that (A) holds for every wff.

The proofs of (i) and (ii) are straightforward, and we omit them here. We prove (iii) by showing, as is clearly sufficient, that, on the hypothesis that (A) holds for α, $V(L\alpha, w) = 0$ iff $V^*(L\alpha, w) = 0$.

Suppose, firstly, that $V(L\alpha, w) = 0$. Then by $[VL]$, $V(\alpha, w') = 0$ for some w' such that wRw'. By the definition of W^*, there is some $u \in W^*$ such that $u \approx w'$, and by the definition of R^*, wR^*u. Moreover, by the definition of $\approx$, we have $V(\alpha, u) = 0$, since $V(\alpha, w') = 0$ and $u \approx w'$. Therefore by the induction hypothesis that (A) holds for α, we have $V^*(\alpha, u) = 0$; and hence, since wR^*u, $V^*(L\alpha, w) = 0$.

Suppose now that $V^*(L\alpha, w) = 0$. Then $V^*(\alpha, w') = 0$ for some $w' \in W^*$ such that wR^*w'. So by the induction hypothesis, $V(\alpha, w') = 0$. Now wR^*w' does not guarantee that wRw', but it does guarantee, by the definition of R^*, that there is some $u \in W$ such that $u \approx w'$ and wRu. So by the definition of $\approx$, since we have $V(\alpha, w') = 0$, we also have $V(\alpha, u) = 0$. Hence by $[VL]$, $V(L\alpha, w) = 0$.

This completes the proof that (A) holds for all wff.

Now $\langle W^*, R^*, V^* \rangle$ is a distinguishable model. For we have chosen the worlds in W^* so that no two of them are equivalent in $\langle W, R, V \rangle$; and (A) then shows that no two of them are equivalent in $\langle W^*, R^*, V^* \rangle$ either. Moreover, $\langle W^*, R^*, V^* \rangle$ and $\langle W, R, V \rangle$ are equivalent models. For since W^* is a subset of W, (A) shows that if α is true everywhere in $\langle W, R, V \rangle$, it is also true everywhere in $\langle W^*, R^*, V^* \rangle$. And conversely, if α is true everywhere in $\langle W^*, R^*, V^* \rangle$, it is true in some world in each equivalence class in W, and therefore true everywhere in $\langle W, R, V \rangle$. Finally, since W^* is a subset of W, it has no more members than W has.

This proves Theorem 5.5.

Certain special kinds of distinguishable models will play an important role later on, in chapter 8.

Generated frames

Some frames are composed of a number of parts, each completely isolated from any of the others. For example, the frame is like this. We shall call such frames, *non-cohesive* frames. By contrast, a *cohesive* frame is one in which each world can see each other world in a number of forward-or-backward R-steps.[4] To give a formal definition, we shall use the notation '$wR^{-1}w'$' to mean that $w'Rw$, and '$w(R \cup R^{-1})w'$' to mean that either wRw' or $w'Rw$. We can then define a *cohesive* frame as one in which, for every w and $w' \in W$, $w(R \cup R^{-1})^n w'$ for some $n \geqslant 0$. For many purposes a non-cohesive frame is most conveniently thought of as a collection of the cohesive frames of which it is composed. Nevertheless, it is certainly a frame, and in some contexts it will be important to think of it as a single one.

Next, sometimes, but not always, a frame has what we might call a 'starting point', i.e. a world which can see every other world in it in some number of steps (though possibly a different number in each case). A frame of this kind is called a *generated* frame.[5] A formal definition is that $\mathscr{F}$ ($= \langle W, R \rangle$) is a *generated* frame iff there is some $w^* \in W$ such that for every $w \in W$, $w^*R^n w$ for some $n \geqslant 0$. Such a w^* is then said to be a *generating world* (for $\mathscr{F}$), and $\mathscr{F}$ is said to be *generated by* w^*. We shall call a model based on a generated frame, a *generated model*.

Note that a frame may have more than one generating world. For example, the frame

is generated both by w_1 and by w_2.

Clearly, every generated frame is cohesive. But a cohesive frame need not be generated. A simple example of a frame which is cohesive but not generated is

Two further points that are worth noting are (a) that a transitive frame (given that it is cohesive) is generated iff there is some world in it which can see (in one step) every other world; and (b) that a symmetrical frame (again, given that it is cohesive) is always generated, and every world in it is a generating world.

Next, if a frame contains a world w^* which can see (in one step) every world in the frame, we shall say that it is *strongly generated* (by w^*). Clearly every reflexive transitive frame which is generated is strongly generated; but a frame can be strongly generated without being either reflexive or transitive. An example would be

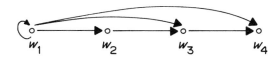

– which is strongly generated by w_1.

Finally, if w^* is any world in any frame $\mathscr{F}$ (whether $\mathscr{F}$ is generated or not, or even whether it is cohesive or not), we can consider the frame obtained from $\mathscr{F}$ by retaining w^* and all the worlds that w^* can see in any number of steps, and deleting all the rest. This frame is called the *sub-frame of $\mathscr{F}$ generated by w^**. More formally, if $\mathscr{F}$ ($= \langle W, R \rangle$) is any frame and w^* is any world in W, then the sub-frame of $\mathscr{F}$ generated by w^* is the frame $\mathscr{F}'$ ($= \langle W', R' \rangle$) in which

  (i) W' is the smallest subset of W satisfying the condition that $w^* \in W'$ and for any $w \in W'$, if wRw', then $w' \in W'$; and

  (ii) R' is simply the restriction of R to W' – i.e. $wR'w'$ iff w and w' are both in W' and wRw'.

We can speak similarly of the *sub-model* of a given model which is generated by a world in that model. Here, of course, we require that the value-assignments to the variables be the same as they are in the original model. That is, if $\langle W, R, V \rangle$ is a model and $w^* \in W$, then the sub-model of $\langle W, R, V \rangle$ generated by w^*, is the model $\langle W', R', V' \rangle$ in which $\langle W', R' \rangle$ is the sub-frame of $\langle W, R \rangle$ generated by w^*, and for every $w \in W'$ and every variable p, $V'(p, w) = V(p, w)$.

It should be clear that in any frame or any model, each world generates a unique sub-frame or sub-model.

We shall now prove some important results about generated frames and generated models. It should be clear from the evaluation rules that in any model, the truth-value of a wff at a world w depends only on the values which formulae have in w itself and in worlds to which it is related in one or more steps, and that the values which formulae have in any other worlds are irrelevant. In other words, the value of a wff at w depends only on the values that formulae have in the sub-model generated by w. We can therefore prove

THEOREM 5.6
If $\langle W, R, V \rangle$ is any model and $\langle W', R', V' \rangle$ is any generated sub-model of $\langle W, R, V \rangle$, then for any wff α, and any $w \in W'$, $V(\alpha, w) = V'(\alpha, w)$.

PROOF
The proof is by induction on the construction of a wff. If α is a variable, the theorem holds by the definition of a sub-model. It is obvious that if $V(\alpha, w) = V'(\alpha, w)$, then $V(\sim \alpha, w) = V'(\sim \alpha, w)$, and also that if $V(\alpha, w) = V'(\alpha, w)$ and $V(\beta, w) = V'(\beta, w)$, then $V(\alpha \lor \beta, w) = V'(\alpha \lor \beta, w)$. For the induction for L, we first note that, by the definition of a sub-model, the worlds that any $w \in W'$ can see in $\langle W', R', V' \rangle$ are precisely those that it can see in $\langle W, R, V \rangle$. We now assume that the theorem holds for a wff α, and show that it then holds for $L\alpha$. By [VL], for any $w \in W'$, $V'(L\alpha, w) = 1$ iff $V'(\alpha, w') = 1$ for every w' that w can see in $\langle W', R', V' \rangle$, and hence for every w' that w can see in $\langle W, R, V \rangle$. By the induction hypothesis, this is so iff $V(\alpha, w') = 1$ for every such w', and hence (by [VL]) iff $V(L\alpha, w) = 1$.

This completes the proof.

Several important consequences follow from this theorem. Consider first the canonical model $\langle W, R, V \rangle$ for a system S. Obviously, if α is a theorem of S, α is true in every $w \in W$, and if α is not a theorem of S, then α is false in some $w \in W$. Hence by Theorem 5.6, in the former case α is true at the generating world of every generated sub-model of $\langle W, R, V \rangle$, and in the latter case α is false at the generating world of some such sub-model. Thus we have

COROLLARY 5.7
If S is any normal modal system, then α is a theorem of S iff α is true at the generating world of every generated sub-model of the canonical model for S.

Further easily derived consequences are:

COROLLARY 5.8
If $\mathscr{F}$ is any frame, then α is valid on $\mathscr{F}$ iff it is valid on every generated sub-frame of $\mathscr{F}$.[6]

COROLLARY 5.9
If $\mathscr{F}$ is any frame, then α is valid on $\mathscr{F}$ iff it is true at the generating world of every model based on every generated sub-frame of $\mathscr{F}$.

COROLLARY 5.10
A normal modal system is characterized by a class of frames $\mathscr{C}$ iff it is characterized by the class of all generated sub-frames of frames in $\mathscr{C}$.

As a special, but very common, case of Corollary 5.10, we have

COROLLARY 5.11
If a normal modal system S is characterized by a class of frames $\mathscr{C}$ which is such that every generated sub-frame of any frame in $\mathscr{C}$ is also itself in $\mathscr{C}$, then S is characterized by the class of all generated frames in $\mathscr{C}$.

Moreover, since every complete system is characterized by the class of all the frames for that system, Corollaries 5.8 and 5.11 yield the result that every complete system is characterized by the class of all generated frames for that system. In fact, more generally, we have

COROLLARY 5.12
If S is any complete normal modal system, then S is characterized by any class of frames for S which contains all the generated frames for S.

We leave the details of the proofs of these last five corollaries as an exercise.

S4.3 reconsidered

In chapter 2 we considered the system S4.3, i.e. S4 +

D1 $L(Lp \supset q) \vee L(Lq \supset p)$

The upshot of our discussion there was that S4.3 is characterized by the class of all models (and this means all *frames*) which are reflexive, transitive, and *connected* in the sense that if $w_1 R w_2$ and $w_1 R w_3$, either $w_2 R w_3$ or $w_3 R w_2$ (or both).

As was noted in *IML* (p. 262), S4.3 has a close connection with the interpretation of L as 'it now is and always will be the case that' and the corresponding interpretation of M as 'it either now is or at some time will be the case that'. In a frame which reflects this interpretation, W will be the set of all moments of time, and wRw' will mean that w is at least as early as w'. The conception of time we have in mind is one in which the moments of time are strung out on a single line, and we want this idea to be reflected in the conditions to be satisfied by R. Obviously, then, R ought to be reflexive and transitive. Moreover, it ought to be connected in a rather stronger sense than the one we have been considering: for we ought to have either $w_2 R w_3$ or $w_3 R w_2$ for *any* pair of moments w_2 and w_3, not merely for those pairs where both members are accessible from some w_1. Let us say that a relation R is *totally connected* (in W) iff it satisfies this condition (i.e. that for any w and $w' \in$ W, either wRw' or $w'Rw$); let us call a relation which is reflexive, transitive and totally connected, a *weak linearity* relation; and let us say that a frame $\langle$ W, R $\rangle$ in which R is such a relation is a *weakly linear* frame. Then we want our frames to be at least weakly linear ones.

In fact we shall want them to satisfy a more stringent condition still. To explain what this is, and incidentally to account for our use of the terms 'weak' and 'weakly', we note that in a weakly linear frame it is possible to have a number of distinct but 'contemporaneous' (i.e. mutually related) worlds or moments, and such a situation seems to be inconsistent with the notion of time that we are trying to capture. To give a clearer idea of what weakly linear frames are like, we introduce the notion of a *cluster*.[7] Suppose that $\langle$ W, R $\rangle$ is a transitive frame. Then a subset A of W is a cluster (in $\langle$ W, R $\rangle$) iff (i) R is a universal relation over A, and (ii) for every $w \in$ W which is not in A, R is not a universal relation over $A \cup \{w\}$. In other words, A is a cluster iff each world in it can see every world in it, and there is no world outside A that can both see and be seen by a world in A. A cluster which contains two or more worlds is called a *proper cluster.* If we use a circle to represent a cluster, then weakly linear frames look like this:

Here the arrows represent the fact that every world in any cluster can see all the worlds in all subsequent clusters. Each cluster can have any number of members, and there may, or may not, be a first cluster or a last cluster. Moreover, despite what the picture may suggest, there may or may not be infinitely many other clusters between any two clusters.

The extra condition we want to impose on our frames is that they should contain no proper clusters; and this means that R should also be *antisymmetrical* in the sense explained on p. 50; i.e. that for any w and $w' \in W$, if both wRw' and $w'Rw$, then $w = w'$. A weakly linear frame which is also antisymmetrical we shall call simply a *linear* frame. By using some of the results we have obtained earlier in this chapter, we can now prove that S4.3 is in fact characterized by the class of all linear frames, and thus that, given the temporal interpretation mentioned above, it is the correct modal logic for a linear conception of time. We shall do this in two stages: (a) we shall use some of our results about generated frames to show that S4.3 is characterized by the class of all weakly linear frames; and then (b) we shall use p-morphisms to show that it is also characterized by the antisymmetrical frames in this class, i.e. by the class of all linear frames.

(a) We know that the class of all reflexive, transitive, connected frames characterizes S4.3. Let us call this class $\mathscr{C}$. Since a totally connected relation is obviously connected, all weakly linear frames are in $\mathscr{C}$, and are therefore frames for S4.3. They are not, however, the only frames for S4.3: the following frame,

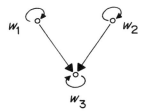

for example, is in $\mathscr{C}$, and so is a frame for S4.3, but it is not weakly linear, since it has neither $w_1 R w_2$ nor $w_2 R w_1$. Corollary 5.10, however, will give us the result we want, if we can show that the class of *generated sub-frames* of frames in $\mathscr{C}$ is the same as the class of all generated sub-frames of weakly linear frames. Now it is easy to see that these are simply the classes of all generated frames in $\mathscr{C}$ and all generated weakly linear frames respectively. Clearly any frame in the latter is in the former, since a totally connected relation is connected. And for the converse, take any $\langle W, R \rangle$ in $\mathscr{C}$ with a generating world w^*. Then since R is reflexive and transitive, we have $w^* R w$ and $w^* R w'$ for any w and $w' \in W$; so, since R is connected, we have either $w R w'$ or $w' R w$, and thus $\langle W, R \rangle$ is weakly linear.

We now turn to the proof of (b). A linear frame, we recall, is one which is reflexive, transitive, totally connected and anti-symmetrical. Obviously, all such frames are reflexive, transitive and connected, and so all the theorems of S4.3 are valid on them. What we still have to prove is that every non-theorem of S4.3 is invalid on some linear frame.

Since, as we have just proved, S4.3 is characterized by the class of all weakly linear frames, every non-theorem of S4.3 is invalid on some frame of this kind. A weakly linear frame differs from a linear one only in that it may contain proper clusters, whereas a linear frame may not. We shall now describe a method of replacing any weakly linear frame by a linear one, in such a way that any formula which is invalid on the former is also invalid on the latter. Clearly this will give us the result we want. This method is due to Segerberg, and he calls it 'bulldozing' because it has the effect of 'flattening out' the clusters in a frame.[8]

We shall first illustrate the technique by a simple example. Consider the following frame $\langle W, R \rangle$, in which R is assumed to be reflexive and transitive:

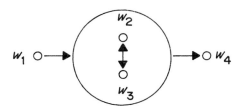

This is a weakly linear frame in which w_2 and w_3 form a proper cluster. To obtain a bulldozed version of it we first make a denumerable infinity of 'copies' of w_2, which we shall refer to as $w_2^1, \ldots, w_2^i, \ldots$, and also a denumerable infinity of 'copies' of $w_3, w_3^1, \ldots, w_3^i, \ldots$. We then string these out in a single line in the following pattern:

$$w_2^1, w_3^1, w_2^2, w_3^2, \ldots, w_2^i, w_3^i, \ldots$$

We finally form our new frame $\langle W^*, R^* \rangle$ by replacing the cluster $\{w_2, w_3\}$ by the sequence just described, and letting each world be related to itself and every subsequent world but to no preceding one. The result is as in the following diagram (where for simplicity the arrows required by reflexiveness and transitivity are omitted):

Clearly this new frame $\langle W^*, R^* \rangle$ is a linear one. We can now define a function f from $\langle W^*, R^* \rangle$ to $\langle W, R \rangle$ by mapping each w_2^i on to w_2, each w_3^i on to w_3, and w_1 and w_4 on to the original w_1 and w_4 respectively. It is then easy to check that f is a p-morphism from $\langle W^*, R^* \rangle$ to $\langle W, R \rangle$. By Theorem 5.3, therefore, any wff which is valid on $\langle W^*, R^* \rangle$ is valid on $\langle W, R \rangle$, and so by contraposition, any wff which is invalid on $\langle W, R \rangle$ is invalid on $\langle W^*, R^* \rangle$.

The result we want is simply a generalization of this one. Suppose that $\langle W, R \rangle$ is any weakly linear frame. It may contain any number of clusters, even non-denumerably many, and each cluster may contain any number of worlds, even non-denumerably many; but the procedure is only an extension of the one we used in the case of $\{w_2, w_3\}$ above. Let A be any proper cluster in $\langle W, R \rangle$, and let its members be arranged in some linear order. For each w in A we make a denumerable infinity of copies, $w^1, w^2, w^3, \ldots$, etc. We then define a linear ordering of all these copies in such a way that w^i precedes v^j if $i < j$, and w^i precedes v^i if w precedes v in the original ordering of A. Finally, we form our new frame $\langle W^*, R^* \rangle$ by replacing each proper cluster in $\langle W, R \rangle$ by an ordering of the kind we have just described, and letting each world in the whole frame be related (by R^*) to itself and every subsequent world but to no others. Again,

$\langle$ W*, R* $\rangle$ is linear. And if we define a function f from $\langle$ W*, R* $\rangle$ to $\langle$ W, R $\rangle$ by mapping each world in W* which is a copy of a world in W on to the world of which it is a copy (and mapping the counterparts of worlds which were not in proper clusters in $\langle$ W, R $\rangle$ simply on to the worlds of which they are counterparts), then f can easily be seen to be a p-morphism from $\langle$ W*, R* $\rangle$ to $\langle$ W, R $\rangle$. So by Theorem 5.3, as before, any wff that is invalid on $\langle$ W, R $\rangle$ is invalid on $\langle$ W*, R* $\rangle$.

The upshot is therefore that since every non-theorem of S4.3 is invalid on some weakly linear frame, every non-theorem is also invalid on some linear frame; and this completes the proof that S4.3 is characterized by the class of all linear frames.

It should be noted that the bulldozing technique which we have just used depends for its success on the fact that the original frame is a transitive one. It does not, however, require that it be either reflexive or connected, and in fact, given any transitive frame $\langle$ W, R $\rangle$ we can by the bulldozing technique, obtain a transitive antisymmetrical frame $\langle$ W*, R* $\rangle$ of which $\langle$ W, R $\rangle$ is a p-morphic image.

The proof we have given that S4.3 is characterized by the class of all linear frames is not the only way of obtaining this result. Later on, in chapter 7, we shall give another proof of it which will be in a sense more direct, in that it will not involve either a consideration of weakly linear frames or the use of p-morphisms. For many of the other results we shall obtain in that chapter, too, the methods to be used there and the bulldozing technique give us alternative ways of establishing the same conclusions.

Exercises – 5

5.1 Prove that if $\mathscr{F}_1$ and $\mathscr{F}_2$ are finite frames and each is a p-morphic image of the other, then they are isomorphic.

5.2 Prove Corollaries 5.8–5.12 on p. 81.

5.3 Use Corollary 5.11 to prove that S5 is characterized by the class of all frames in which R is universal (i.e. in which for all w and $w' \in$ W, wRw').

5.4 Prove that no single cohesive frame characterizes **KE** ($\mathbf{K} + \sim Lp \supset L \sim Lp$).

5.5 Prove that if α is valid on any frame, then α is valid either on the frame $\langle \{w\}, \langle w, w \rangle \rangle$ (i.e. the one-world reflexive frame which characterizes Triv) or on the frame $\langle \{w\}, \varnothing \rangle$ (i.e. the one-world irreflexive frame which characterizes Ver).

5.6 (a) Prove that S4.3 is characterized by the class of all weakly linear frames in which there is no first or last cluster.

(b) Prove that S4.3 is characterized by the class of all weakly linear frames in which there is a first cluster but no last cluster.

5.7 Use the bulldozing technique to prove that S4 is characterized by the class of all frames in which **R** is a partial ordering (i.e. is reflexive, transitive and antisymmetrical).

Notes

1 Segerberg (1968a), pp. 13f. The term 'p-morphism' is used in Segerberg (1971), p. 37.

2 We adopt this terminology from Segerberg (1971), p. 29. Segerberg proves on pp. 29f. that every model is equivalent to a distinguishable model. Cf. our Theorem 5.5, p. 76. The natural models referred to in note 2, p. 66, are in fact distinguishable models which possess an extra feature which is also possessed by canonical models.

3 Many authors (e.g. Segerberg (1971)) take the equivalence classes themselves as the members of **W***. We have, however, thought that it is simpler to take a 'representative' from each of these classes instead, and in this way make the new model as like the original one as possible. In consequence, of course, our definitions of **R*** and **V*** differ in corresponding ways from those given by the other authors in question. Note that if the number of equivalence classes is infinite, our definition of **W*** will in some cases require the Axiom of Choice.

4 The term 'connected' has often been used as we use 'cohesive' here (first, apparently, by Kripke, and then by Lemmon and Scott – see their (1977), p. 25, and n. 18 on that page). Since this use of 'connected' may lead to confusion with the quite different use explained on p. 30, we have thought that another word would be desirable. 'Cohesive' is our own suggestion.

5 See Lemmon and Scott (1977), pp. 25f.

6 This shows that the operation of forming a generated sub-frame preserves validity, in the sense that if $\mathscr{F}'$ is a generated sub-frame of $\mathscr{F}$, then any wff which are valid on $\mathscr{F}$ are also valid on $\mathscr{F}'$. A result of this kind is known as a *preservation theorem*. Another preservation theorem in modal logic is Theorem 5.3; for that theorem shows that the operation of forming a p-morphic image of a frame also preserves validity. One application of preservation theorems is to be found in attempts to solve the problem

of what are the general conditions under which a class $\mathscr{C}$ of frames is such that there is some collection of wff which are valid on all and only those frames which are members of $\mathscr{C}$. This and allied problems lie outside the scope of the present book. The interested reader will find information about them, and further references, in Goldblatt and Thomason (1975) and van Benthem (1979a) and (1980).

7 See Segerberg (1971), p. 75.

8 Segerberg (1971), p. 78. We describe the technique as applied to frames; Segerberg himself defines it in terms of models. His 'Bulldozer Theorem' is stated on p. 80, with an important corollary on p. 81.

6 Frames and systems

In this chapter we continue our investigation of the relation between frames on the one hand and systems on the other.

It is obvious that if a system S is characterized by a class $\mathscr{C}$ of frames, then every frame in $\mathscr{C}$ must be a frame for S, in the sense that every theorem of S is valid on it. But we have seen that one and the same system may be characterized by a number of different classes of frames; so the fact that S is characterized by $\mathscr{C}$ does not guarantee that $\mathscr{C}$ contains *all* the frames for S. For some purposes, however, it is important to know what is the class of all the frames for a given system, and the first part of this chapter is concerned with how we can discover this.

We then turn to consider the frames of canonical models in particular. Although we have already said a good deal about canonical models themselves, we have so far said only a little about their frames. We shall now, however, be able to establish certain results about these, e.g. that some of them are generated but others are not. We shall also be able to prove the perhaps surprising result mentioned on p. 57, that although of course the canonical model for S is always a *model for S*, yet, even if S is a complete system, the frame of its canonical model may not be a frame for S at all; in other words, that a system may be complete but not canonical.

We finally discuss a property which is closely related to

canonicity, viz. *compactness*. What it means for a system S to be compact is that all the formulae in any S-consistent set of formulae can be true together at some world in some frame for S. As with canonicity, it turns out that not every complete system is compact, though most of the well-known ones are.

Frames for T, S4, B and S5

As we have just recalled, by a *frame for* a normal modal system S we mean a frame on which every theorem of S is valid (i.e. true in every world in every model based on it). We also showed, on p. 55, that validity on a frame is preserved by the rules US, MP and N. This means that a frame is a frame for S iff each *axiom* of S is valid on that frame; and in fact we need only consider the modal axioms other than **K**, since **K** is valid on every frame whatsoever.

In our soundness and completeness proofs in chapters 1 and 2 we were able to show that the system T and the class of reflexive models match each other in the sense that any wff is a theorem of T iff it is valid in every reflexive model. Now in saying that a model is reflexive we are speaking only of W and R, not of V, for what we mean is that for every $w \in W$, wRw. Reflexiveness, that is, is a property not so much of a model as of a frame; and we could express our earlier result by saying that T is characterized by the class of all reflexive *frames*. That is certainly one connection between T and the class of all reflexive frames. The question we now want to ask, however, is whether the class of all *frames for T* is the same as the class of all reflexive frames. The answer is that in fact it is. We have, indeed, proved one half of this already. For in proving the soundness of T we showed that every theorem of T is valid in every reflexive model, and therefore on every reflexive frame; and that is just another way of saying that every reflexive frame is a frame for T. But we have not yet proved the other half, namely that every frame for T is reflexive. It is, however, quite easy to do so.

THEOREM 6.1
Every frame for T is reflexive.

PROOF
The proof is by contraposition; i.e. we shall show that if any

frame $\mathscr{F}$ is not reflexive, then some theorem of T – in fact $Lp \supset p$ – is not valid on $\mathscr{F}$. Suppose then that $\mathscr{F}$ is not reflexive. This means that some $w \in W$ is not related to itself. Let w^* be such a world. Then let $\langle \mathscr{F}, V \rangle$ be a model based on $\mathscr{F}$ in which $V(p, w^*) = 0$ but $V(p, w) = 1$ for every $w \in W$ *except* w^*. Since w^* is not related to itself, this will make p true in every world to which w^* *is* related. Thus $V(Lp, w^*) = 1$. But $V(p, w^*) = 0$. Hence $V(Lp \supset p, w^*) = 0$. So $Lp \supset p$ is not valid in this model, and therefore is not valid on $\mathscr{F}$.

This completes the proof of Theorem 6.1. It and the soundness of T then give us

COROLLARY 6.2
$\mathscr{F}$ is a frame for T iff $\mathscr{F}$ is reflexive.

It is important to note that Theorem 6.1 holds only for frames, not for models. That is, it is not the case that every *model* for T is reflexive, even though every reflexive model is a model for T. To see this, consider a frame $\langle W, R \rangle$ in which $W = \{w_1, w_2\}$ and $R = \{\langle w_1, w_2 \rangle, \langle w_2, w_1 \rangle\}$ – i.e. a two-world frame in which neither world can see itself but each can see the other. We could picture the frame in this way:

Now consider any model based on this frame in which each variable has the same value in both worlds, i.e. any model in which $V(p, w_1) = V(p, w_2)$ for each variable p. It is not hard to prove, by induction on the construction of a wff, that for every wff α, $V(\alpha, w_1) = V(\alpha, w_2)$. We now show that for any wff α, $V(L\alpha \supset \alpha, w_1) = 1$. For suppose that $V(L\alpha, w_1) = 1$. Then since $w_1 R w_2$, we have $V(\alpha, w_2) = 1$; and hence, since α has the same value at both worlds, $V(\alpha, w_1) = 1$. Clearly an exactly similar argument will show that $V(L\alpha \supset \alpha, w_2) = 1$. This means that every substitution-instance of **T** is valid in the model in question, and therefore, by Theorem 1.2, that it is a model for T. But clearly it is not a reflexive model.[1]

A model of the kind we have just described is in fact constructed out of a one-world reflexive model by the method for producing irreflexive models described on p. 48. As we observed there, the fact that this method can be applied to any model whatsoever shows that *at the level of models* irreflexiveness has no semantic effect, in the sense that for any model there will always be an irreflexive model in which precisely the same wff are valid. At the level of frames, however, the position is different. The proof given on pp. 48f. does indeed show that even at this level irreflexiveness has no semantic effect *on its own*, because irreflexive frames are still frames for K. But in combination with other conditions irreflexiveness certainly can have a semantic effect at the level of frames. For example, as Theorem 6.1 shows, there are no irreflexive frames for T at all; the system characterized by the class of irreflexive frames for T is therefore not T but the inconsistent system.

Theorem 6.1 and Corollary 6.2 should be compared with Theorem 2.9 on p. 28. That theorem, in conjunction with the soundness of T, establishes that T is characterized by the class of all reflexive frames. But this by itself does not give us Corollary 6.2. For, as we have seen on p. 49, it is perfectly possible for a system to be characterized by a class of frames $\mathscr{C}$, and also by another class which contains frames that are not in $\mathscr{C}$. So the mere fact that T is characterized by the class of all reflexive frames still leaves open the possibility that it might also be characterized by some class of frames which contains, or even consists solely of, non-reflexive ones. And it is this which Corollary 6.2 assures us cannot be so. For the proof of Theorem 6.1 shows that $Lp \supset p$ fails on *every* non-reflexive frame, and therefore that no such frame can be a member of *any* class which characterizes T. In other words, every class of frames which characterizes T must consist solely of reflexive frames.

Theorem 6.1, therefore, establishes something that Theorem 2.9 does not. Does this mean that it is *stronger* than Theorem 2.9, that it proves all that that theorem proves and more besides? If it did, that would indeed be gratifying, since the proof of Theorem 6.1 is a great deal simpler than a completeness proof by canonical models. Unfortunately, however, there is no short cut to a completeness proof by this method. Certainly, *if T is characterized by any class of frames at all*, then it will be characterized by the class of all frames for T, and then Corollary 6.2 assures us that in that case it is characterized by the class of all reflexive frames. But the hypothesis here is that T *is* characterized by some class of frames; and that is something that Corollary 6.2 does not tell us, and which we need a separate proof to establish.

To make the position clearer, consider again the incomplete system VB. What we proved in chapter 4 is that the system characterized by the class of all frames for VB is stronger than VB itself, because it contains the wff **MV**, which is not a theorem of VB. So although it is true that a frame is a frame for VB (a frame on which every theorem of VB is valid) iff it is a frame in which every world either is a dead end or can see some dead end – which gives us an analogue of Corollary 6.2 for VB – it is *not* true that VB is characterized by the class of all such frames.

What all this means is that the fact that the frames for a certain system are precisely the frames which have a certain property, is neither a necessary nor a sufficient condition of that system's being characterized by the class of all frames which have that property. The case of VB shows that it is not a sufficient condition; and the fact that K is characterized by the class of all irreflexive frames but that not all frames for K are irreflexive, shows that it is not a necessary condition either. The most that we can say is that *if* a system S is complete, in the sense of being characterized by some class of frames, and *if* the frames for S are precisely those that possess a certain property, then the class of all frames with that property is one of the classes of frames (and in fact the largest of them) which characterize S.

We have gone through the situation in some detail for T. For S4, B and S5 we shall merely survey the analogous results. These are that the frames for S4 are precisely those that are reflexive and transitive, that the frames for B are precisely those that are reflexive and symmetrical, and that the frames for S5 are precisely those that are reflexive, transitive and symmetrical. S4, of course, is $T + 4$ ($Lp \supset LLp$); B is $T + \mathbf{B}(\sim p \supset L \sim Lp)$; and S5, although in chapter 1 we axiomatized it as $T + \mathbf{E}$, can equally well be axiomatized as $T + 4 + \mathbf{B}$. So, since we have already proved the soundness of these systems, all that we still have to do is to prove that every frame on which **4** is valid is transitive, and that every frame on which **B** is valid is symmetrical.

THEOREM 6.3
Every frame on which $Lp \supset LLp$ is valid is transitive.

PROOF
Let $\mathscr{F}$ be any non-transitive frame. This means that there are worlds w_1, w_2 and w_3 in W such that $w_1 R w_2$ and $w_2 R w_3$ but not $w_1 R w_3$. Let $\langle \mathscr{F}, V \rangle$ be a model based on $\mathscr{F}$ in which $V(p, w_3) = 0$ but $V(p, w) = 1$ for every $w \in W$ other than w_3. Then clearly $V(Lp, w_1) = 1$. However, $V(Lp, w_2) = 0$, and hence $V(LLp, w_1) = 0$. So $V(Lp \supset LLp, w_1) = 0$, which means that $Lp \supset LLp$ is not valid on $\mathscr{F}$.

THEOREM 6.4
Every frame on which $\sim p \supset L \sim Lp$ is valid is symmetrical.

PROOF
Let $\mathscr{F}$ be any non-symmetrical frame. This means that there are worlds w_1 and w_2 in W such that $w_1 R w_2$ but not $w_2 R w_1$. Let $\langle \mathscr{F}, V \rangle$ be a model based on $\mathscr{F}$ in which $V(p, w_1) = 0$ but $V(p, w) = 1$ for every $w \in W$ other than w_1. Then (a) $V(\sim p, w_1) = 1$. But since w_2 is not related to w_1, p is true in every world to which w_2 *is* related. So we have $V(Lp, w_2) = 1$, and therefore $V(\sim Lp, w_2) = 0$. Hence, since $w_1 R w_2$, we have (b) $V(L \sim Lp, w_1) = 0$. (a) and (b) then give us the result that $V(\sim p \supset L \sim Lp, w_1) = 0$, and so $\sim p \supset L \sim Lp$ is not valid on $\mathscr{F}$.

We can prove analogous results for many other formulae and systems than the ones we have just dealt with. For example, we can prove that every frame on which **D1** (see p. 30) is valid is connected. The proof is that if any frame contains worlds w_1, w_2 and w_3 such that $w_1 R w_2$ and $w_1 R w_3$ but neither $w_2 R w_3$ nor $w_3 R w_2$, then a model based on that frame which makes p false at w_3 but true everywhere else, and q false at w_2 but true everywhere else, will make **D1** false at w_1.

The frames of canonical models

The canonical model for a given modal system, like any other model, is based on a certain frame. So far we have said a good deal about canonical models, but very little about the frames on which they are based, except to note that, although every normal system is characterized by its canonical model, it does not follow that every such system is characterized by the frame of its canonical model, because that frame may not be a frame for the system at all. (Obviously, if the frame of the canonical model for S is a frame for S, then that frame characterizes S.) We shall now say something more about the frames of canonical models; in particular, we shall enquire, about a number of them, whether or not they are cohesive, and if they are cohesive, whether or not they are also generated. The notions of cohesive and generated frames were explained in the previous chapter (p. 78).

It is easy to see that the frames of *some* canonical models are not cohesive. An extreme example is provided by the Verum system. We showed on pp. 34f. that in the canonical model for this system each world is a dead end. The frame of this model therefore consists of a collection of worlds none of which is related to itself or to any of the others, and is thus as radically non-cohesive as any frame could be. We may, indeed, feel that it is more natural to regard it as a collection of distinct frames than as a single frame; and in fact the Verum system is characterized not only by the frame of its canonical model but also by the frame which consists of a single dead end. There is, however, this important difference between these two frames, that whereas there is a model based on the former (viz. the canonical model) which characterizes Ver, there can be no model based on the latter which does so. The reason is that in any model based on a one-world frame, either p is true in every world or else $\sim p$ is true in every world; yet neither p nor $\sim p$ is a theorem of Ver. The case of the Trivial system is analogous. The frame of the canonical model for Triv consists of a collection of worlds each of which can see itself but none of the others. Triv is characterized both by this frame and by a one-world reflexive frame; but, for the same reason as in the case of Ver, it is characterized by a model based on the former, but not by any model based on the latter.

Another canonical model whose frame is not cohesive is the canonical model for S5. This is not as obvious as for Ver or Triv, but in fact the frame of this model is split up into a number of disjoint sets of worlds, each isolated from all the others. The relation R is universal within each such set (i.e. each world is related to every world in its own set), but it is not universal over the whole frame. How do we know that the frame of the canonical model for S5 is like this? One simple proof is this: p is an S5-consistent wff, and therefore is true in some world in the canonical model for S5. Now if R were universal in that model, then Mp would be true in *every* world in it; and therefore, by Corollary 2.5, it would be a theorem of S5. But we know that it is not.

At this point one might perhaps begin to suspect that the frame of the canonical model for a normal modal system is never a cohesive frame, or at least never a generated one. Canonical models, after all, are *very* large, and it might seem natural to expect that they would all contain some isolated sub-models, or at least would not contain any generating worlds. However, for a quite wide range of systems we can prove that the frames of their canonical models are not merely generated but even strongly generated in the sense explained on p. 79. In particular, this will be so for any system S in which the following rule, which we call the *rule of disjunction*, holds:

$$\text{RD} \quad \vdash_S L\alpha_1 \vee \ldots \vee L\alpha_n \rightarrow \vdash_S \alpha_i \text{ for some } i(1 \leqslant i \leqslant n)$$

Using the terminology of Lemmon and Scott,[2] we shall say that a system in which this rule holds *provides the rule of disjunction*.

THEOREM 6.5
Suppose that S is a normal modal system which provides the rule of disjunction. Then the frame of the canonical model for S is strongly generated.

PROOF
Let S be any such system. We first show that the following set of wff is S-consistent:

$$\{ \sim L\alpha : \dashv_S \alpha \}$$

The proof is this: suppose that this set is not S-consistent. Then for some $\alpha_1, \ldots, \alpha_n$, none of which is a theorem of S,

$$\vdash_S \sim (\sim L\alpha_1 . \ldots . \sim L\alpha_n)$$

Hence by PC,

$$\vdash_S L\alpha_1 \vee \ldots \vee L\alpha_n$$

But by hypothesis S provides the rule of disjunction. Therefore

$\vdash_S \alpha_i$ for some i $(1 \leqslant i \leqslant n)$. But this contradicts the assumption that no such α_i is a theorem of S.

Since, then, $\{ \sim L\alpha : \dashv_S \alpha \}$ is S-consistent, there will be some world, say w^*, in the canonical model for S, which includes it. Thus for every wff α, if α is not a theorem of S, then $\sim L\alpha \in w^*$, and hence $L\alpha \notin w^*$. It follows that if $L\alpha \in w^*$, then α is a theorem of S, and therefore is in every $w \in W$. This means that $L^-(w^*)$ is included in every $w \in W$. So we have $w^* R w$ for every $w \in W$; that is, the frame is strongly generated.

This ends the proof.

Among the systems which can be shown to provide the rule of disjunction are K, D, T and S4. On the other hand, no (consistent) system which contains either B or S4.2 provides it; for $LM \sim p \vee LMp$ is a theorem both of B and of S4.2, but neither $M \sim p$ nor Mp is a theorem of either of these systems or of any consistent extensions of them. This might suggest the general principle that if a system does not provide the rule, then neither does any of its extensions, and by consequence that if a system does provide the rule, then so does every system that it contains. This principle, however, does not hold universally. Consider the system K +

(1) $L(Lp \supset p) \vee L(Lp \supset LLp)$

Since the first disjunct in (1) is obviously a theorem of T, so is (1) itself; so K + (1) lies between K and T. Yet both K and T provide the rule, but K + (1) does not. The proof is this: consider any frame that is transitive but not reflexive. This is a frame for K + (1), since the second disjunct in (1), and therefore (1) itself, is valid on it. But it is not a frame for $Lp \supset p$, because it is not reflexive (see Theorem 6.1). Therefore $Lp \supset p$ is not a theorem of K + (1). Consider now any frame which is reflexive but not transitive. This is also a frame for K + (1), because the first disjunct in (1) is valid on it. But it is not a frame for $Lp \supset LLp$ (see Theorem 6.3), and so $Lp \supset LLp$ is not a theorem of K + (1). Thus since (1) is a theorem of K + (1) but neither $Lp \supset p$ nor $Lp \supset LLp$ is, the system does not provide the rule of disjunction. The proof that both K and T provide the rule will be given in the next section.

Establishing the rule of disjunction

We have shown in the last section that certain systems do not provide the rule of disjunction. In this section we shall show that certain other systems do provide it. Our method will be first of all to prove that any system which satisfies a certain semantic condition provides the rule, and then to show that certain systems do satisfy this condition.[3]

In order to be able to state this condition, we first define the operation of producing a model which is an *amalgamation* of a given finite collection of models. Briefly, such an amalgamation is produced by simply adding an extra world which is related to all the worlds in each of the original models. To express this more formally: suppose we have n models,

$$\langle W_1, R_1, V_1 \rangle, \dots, \langle W_n, R_n, V_n \rangle$$

We shall assume that no two of these models have any worlds in common – we lose no generality for our present purposes by this assumption, since if any pair do have any worlds in common, we can always replace one of them by an isomorphic copy of it, using a fresh set of worlds. Then an *amalgamation* of these models is a model $\langle W, R, V \rangle$ defined as follows:

(1) W is the union of all the W_i s ($1 \leqslant i \leqslant n$), together with a single world w^* which is not a member of any w_i.
(2) R must satisfy the following conditions:
    (a) For any w and $w' \in W_i$, wRw' iff wR_iw';
    (b) For any $w \in W_i$, w^*Rw_i.

(Thus the relations within each original model are preserved unchanged, and in addition w^* is related to every world in each of the original models. This definition leaves it open whether or not w^*Rw^*, but otherwise determines R completely.)

(3) For any variable p and any $w \in W_i$, $V(p, w) = V_i(p, w)$. The value-assignment to the variables in w^* is arbitrary. (I.e. we leave the original value-assignments unaltered, and give any value-assignments we choose at w^*.)

It should be clear that since the only new world in such an amalgamation (w^*) is not accessible from any world in any of the original models, its addition cannot change the truth-value of any wff in any world in those models.

We can now prove

THEOREM 6.6
Suppose that S is a normal system, and that there is some class $\mathscr{C}$ of generated models such that (a) every wff which is not a theorem of S is false at a generating world of some model in $\mathscr{C}$, and (b) every finite subset of $\mathscr{C}$ has an amalgamation which is a model for S. Then S provides the rule of disjunction.

PROOF
The proof proceeds by showing that, given the hypothesis of the theorem, if none of $\alpha_1, \ldots, \alpha_n$ is a theorem of S, neither is $L\alpha_1 \vee \ldots \vee L\alpha_n$. Suppose, then, that none of $\alpha_1, \ldots, \alpha_n$ is a theorem of S. Then there is in $\mathscr{C}$ a collection of models $\langle W_1, R_1, V_1 \rangle, \ldots, \langle W_n, R_n, V_n \rangle$, generated by $w_1, \ldots, w_n$ respectively, such that for each $i(1 \leqslant i \leqslant n)$, $V_i(\alpha_i, w_i) = 0$; and moreover there is an amalgamation $\langle W, R, V \rangle$ of $\{\langle W_1, R_1, V_1 \rangle, \ldots, \langle W_n, R_n, V_n \rangle\}$ which is a model for S. Hence by Theorem 5.6 (p. 80) we have (in $\langle W, R, V \rangle$) $V(\alpha_i, w_i) = 0$ for each i; and by the definition of an amalgamation we have w^*Rw_i, again for each i. Therefore we have $V(L\alpha_i, w^*) = 0$, for each i, and so $V(L\alpha_1 \vee \ldots \vee L\alpha_n, w^*) = 0$. But $\langle W, R, V \rangle$ is a model for S. Therefore $L\alpha_1 \vee \ldots \vee L\alpha_n$ is not a theorem of S.

This ends the proof.

We have stated Theorem 6.6 in terms of models rather than frames in order to make it applicable to systems which are not complete, or which are not known to be complete. We can, however, speak in an obvious sense of an amalgamation of a finite collection of *frames* rather than models. We can then prove

THEOREM 6.7
Suppose that S is a complete normal modal system and that every finite collection of frames for S has an amalgamation which is itself a frame for S. Then S provides the rule of disjunction.

PROOF
By Corollary 5.12 (p. 81), S is characterized by the class of all generated frames for S. Let $\mathscr{C}$ be the class of all models based on such frames. Then by Corollary 5.9, any non-theorem of S is

false at a generating world in some model in $\mathscr{C}$. Moreover, since every model in $\mathscr{C}$ is based on a frame for S, any finite subset of such models will (by the hypothesis of the theorem) have an amalgamation whose frame is also a frame for S, and therefore that amalgamation will be a model for S. Thus $\mathscr{C}$ satisfies the hypothesis of Theorem 6.6, and so, by that theorem, S provides the rule of disjunction.

This ends the proof.

Theorem 6.7 shows immediately that K provides the rule of disjunction, simply because any amalgamation of frames is itself a frame, and every frame is a frame for K. Moreover, any collection of reflexive frames will have *an* amalgamation in which R is reflexive, namely the one in which w^*Rw^*; and clearly every amalgamation of transitive frames is itself transitive. So T, K4 and S4 also provide the rule.

On the other hand, an amalgamation of symmetrical frames is not itself symmetrical. For there is nothing in the procedure of amalgamation to give us wRw^* for any w except possibly w^* itself, though of course we have w^*Rw for every w in each of the original frames. And as we saw on p. 97, the system B does *not* provide the rule of disjunction.

A complete but non-canonical system

As we explained in chapter 4 (p. 56), we say that a system S is *canonical* iff the frame of its canonical model is a frame for S; that is, iff every theorem of S is valid not merely in the canonical model for S itself, but also in every other model that could be based on the frame of that model. We also noted that one of the simplest methods of proving that a system is complete – the method that we have in fact regularly used – amounts to showing that it is canonical. Thus every canonical system is complete, and so every incomplete system – VB for example – is non-canonical. However, the converse of this does not hold, for it is possible for a system to be non-canonical and yet complete. What this means is that the system is characterized by *some* class or classes of frames but that the frame of its canonical model is not a member of any such characterizing class.

An example of such a system is the system KW, which is K with the addition of

W $L(Lp \supset p) \supset Lp$[4]

We shall prove in chapter 8 that KW is characterized by the class of all strict finite partially ordered frames (i.e. frames in which W is finite and R is transitive and irreflexive), and therefore that it is complete. At present we shall confine ourselves to proving that it is not canonical.

We first prove that $Lp \supset LLp$ is a theorem of KW, so that the system is in fact an extension of K4.[5] The proof is this:

PC: (1) $p \supset ((Lp.LLp) \supset (p.Lp))$
(1) × DR1 × L-distribution:
$\qquad$ (2) $Lp \supset L(L(p.Lp) \supset (p.Lp))$
× **W**: $\qquad \supset L(p.Lp)$
× K: $\qquad \supset LLp$

We next prove

LEMMA 6.8
KW provides the rule of disjunction.

PROOF
Let $\mathscr{C}$ be the class of all generated sub-models of the canonical model for KW. We shall show that $\mathscr{C}$ satisfies the hypothesis of Theorem 6.6.

Corollary 5.7 shows that $\mathscr{C}$ satisfies clause (a) of that hypothesis. So all that remains is to show that it also satisfies clause (b) – that is that every finite subset of $\mathscr{C}$ has an amalgamation which is a model for KW.

Let $\langle W_1, R_1, V_1 \rangle, ..., \langle W_n, R_n, V_n \rangle$ be the members of any such subset, and let $\langle W, R, V \rangle$ be an amalgamation of them in which w^* is not related to itself. By Theorem 5.6, every substitution-instance of **W** is true in every $w \in W$ other than w^*. So by Theorem 1.2, all we still have to prove, in order to show that $\langle W, R, V \rangle$ is a model for KW, is that every substitution-instance of **W** is true in w^* as well. We do this by assuming that for some wff α,

(1) $V(L(L\alpha \supset \alpha), w^*) = 1$

and proving that in that case, $V(L\alpha, w^*) = 1$. Since w^* can see every $w \in W$ except itself, (1) gives us

(2) $V(L\alpha \supset \alpha, w) = 1$ for every $w \in W$ other than w^*.

Now consider any $\langle W_i, R_i, V_i \rangle$ $(1 \leqslant i \leqslant n)$, and let w_i be its generating world. By (2), $L\alpha \supset \alpha$ is true in every world that w_i can see (since it cannot see w^*); therefore we have $V(L(L\alpha \supset \alpha)$, $w_i) = 1$, and so by **W**,

    (3) $V(L\alpha, w_i) = 1$.

Now we proved above that $\vdash_{\mathbf{KW}} Lp \supset LLp$; therefore each R_i is transitive. So from (3) we have $V(\alpha, w) = 1$ for every $w \in W_i$ other than w_i. However, (2) and (3) give us $V(\alpha, w_i) = 1$ as well. Hence we have $V(\alpha, w) = 1$ for every $w \in W_i$, and therefore for every $w \in W$ other than w^*. So, since w^* is not related to itself, we have $V(L\alpha, w^*) = 1$, as required. This proves that $\langle W, R, V \rangle$ is a model for KW, and hence that $\mathscr{C}$ satisfies clause (b) of the hypothesis of Theorem 6.6. So by that theorem, KW provides the rule of disjunction.

This completes the proof of the lemma.

The proof that KW is non-canonical is now straightforward. By Lemma 6.8 and Theorem 6.5, the frame of the canonical model for KW is strongly generated. It therefore contains at least one world which can see itself (any generating world will be such a world). But we can show that **W** fails on any frame which contains any world which can see itself. For let $\mathscr{F}$ be such a frame and w^* such a world, and consider a model based on $\mathscr{F}$ in which $V(p, w^*) = 0$ and $V(p, w) = 1$ for every $w \in W$ other than w^*. Then clearly

    (1) $V(Lp, w^*) = 0$

and so

    (2) $V(Lp \supset p, w^*) = 1$.

But, since p is true at all worlds other than w^*, we also have

    (3) $V(Lp \supset p, w) = 1$ for every $w \in W$ other than w^*.

Hence by (2) and (3) we have $V(Lp \supset p, w) = 1$ for every $w \in W$, and therefore

    (4) $V(L(Lp \supset p), w^*) = 1$.

But (4) and (1) mean that **W** is false at w^*, and thus that it fails on $\mathscr{F}$.

Since the only assumption we have made about $\mathscr{F}$ is that it contains some world that can see itself, and since the canonical model for KW contains such a world, we have shown that **W** is not valid on the frame of the canonical model for KW. That is, we have proved

THEOREM 6.9
KW is not canonical.[6]

Compactness
The kind of proof we have just given that KW is not canonical is not the only way of proving the non-canonicity of a system. Another method is to show that the system lacks a property which, following Fine, we call *compactness*.[7] We shall now explain what this property is.

If a wff α is true at some world in some model based on a certain frame $\langle$ W, R $\rangle$, we shall say that α is *satisfiable* in $\langle$ W, R $\rangle$; and if all the wff in a set Λ of wff are true at the same world in some model based on $\langle$ W, R $\rangle$, we shall say that Λ is *simultaneously satisfiable* in $\langle$ W, R $\rangle$. It is easy to see that each wff in a set Λ might be satisfiable in a certain frame, but Λ not be simultaneously satisfiable in that frame. To take a simple example, each of the wff Mp and $M \sim p$ is true at w_1 in some model based on the frame

– the former in a model in which p is true at w_2 and the latter in one in which p is false at w_2 – but there is no model based on this frame in which both wff are true at w_1 (or at w_2 either, since w_2 is a dead end); so the set $\{Mp, M \sim p\}$ is not simultaneously satisfiable in this frame.

Now if S is a complete system, it follows that each S-consistent wff must be satisfiable in some frame for S. For if a wff α is not satisfiable in *any* frame for S, this means that $\sim \alpha$ is valid on every frame for S; and in that case, since S is complete, $\sim \alpha$ is a theorem of S, which is just what we mean by saying that α is not S-consistent.

It follows from this in turn that, again if S is a complete system, every *finite* S-consistent set of wff is simultaneously satisfiable in some frame for S; for we equate the S-consistency of a finite set with the S-consistency of the conjunction of all its members, which is of course itself a wff. But it does not follow that every *infinite* S-consistent set of wff is simultaneously satisfiable in some frame for S. For we equate the S-consistency of an infinite set, not with the S-consistency of the conjunction of all its members – since there is no such thing – but with the S-consistency of each of its finite subsets. And it can happen, with certain systems, that there is a set of wff, Λ, such that every finite subset of Λ is S-consistent (and therefore Λ itself is S-consistent), and yet, while each finite subset of Λ is simultaneously satisfiable in some frame for S, Λ itself is not simultaneously satisfiable in any such frame. When this situation obtains, we say that S is non-compact; otherwise, i.e. if every S-consistent set of wff is simultaneously satisfiable in some frame for S, we say that S is *compact*. The formal definition is this:

If S is a normal modal system, then S is *compact* iff, for every S-consistent set of wff, Λ, there is some model $\langle W, R, V \rangle$ based on a frame for S, in which there is some $w \in W$ such that for every wff $\alpha \in \Lambda$, $V(\alpha, w) = 1$.

It is obvious that every system which is canonical is compact. For by Theorem 2.2, for any normal system, every S-consistent set of wff is a subset of some maximal S-consistent set, and therefore a subset of some world in the canonical model for S. So by the fundamental theorem (2.4), every S-consistent set has all its members true together at some world in the canonical model for S – i.e. is simultaneously satisfiable in the frame of that model. Thus if that frame is a frame for S, which is what we mean by saying that S is canonical, the compactness of S then follows immediately.

We cannot, of course, infer from this that the converse also holds, i.e. that every compact system is canonical. In fact, as far as we know, it is still an open question whether or not this is so. Still, the fact that every canonical system is compact opens up an alternative way of showing that a system is not canonical, viz. by proving that it is not compact.

Our first example of a system which we shall prove to be non-compact is one which Segerberg has called K4.3W.[8] This is KW with the addition of the axiom

D1₀ $L((Lp.p) \supset q) \lor L((Lq.q) \supset p)$

D1₀ is, in the absence of **T**, a kind of weakened version of **D1**, and has an analogous semantic effect, in that it imposes a certain kind of connectedness on frames which are not reflexive. (If we were to add **D1** itself to KW, we should obtain the Verum system; for **D1** $[p/q]$ gives $L(Lp \supset p) \lor L(Lp \supset p)$, and therefore $L(Lp \supset p)$, and therefore, by **W**, Lp. But K4.3W is intermediate between KW and Ver.) The semantic condition which corresponds to **D1₀** and which therefore characterizes $K + D1₀$ is one which is sometimes called *weak connectedness*, i.e. the condition that for any $w_1, w_2, w_3 \in W$,

If $w_1 R w_2$ and $w_1 R w_3$, then either $w_2 = w_3$ *or* $w_2 R w_3$
or $w_3 R w_2$.

We leave it to the reader to prove that $K + D1₀$ is characterized by this condition. For our present purposes the relevant point is that **D1₀** can be falsified on any frame which is not weakly connected. The proof of this is very similar to one we gave for **D1** and non-connected frames on p. 94: if $\langle W, R \rangle$ contains any worlds w_1, w_2 and w_3 such that $w_1 R w_2$ and $w_1 R w_3$, but neither $w_2 = w_3$ nor $w_2 R w_3$ nor $w_3 R w_2$, then in a model based on that frame in which q is false at w_2 but true everywhere else and p is false at w_3 but true everywhere else, **D1₀** is false at w_1.

We can now see that every frame for K4.3W must be irreflexive, transitive and weakly connected. For, as we showed in the proof of the non-canonicity of KW, **W** can be falsified on any frame which has even a single world that is related to itself; by Theorem 6.3, $Lp \supset LLp$, which is a theorem of KW, is falsifiable on any non-transitive frame; and as we have just shown, **D1₀** can be falsified on any frame that is not weakly connected. Now any generated frame which is irreflexive, transitive and weakly connected (and generated frames are the only ones we need to consider) must, unless it consists of a single dead end, consist of a number of worlds all strung out on a single line. A frame of this kind is known as a *strict linear ordering*. Moreover, to be a frame for K4.3W, such a frame must be finite; for on an infinite one we can falsify **W** by letting p be false at all those worlds which can see infinitely many worlds, and true at all those worlds (if there are any) which can see only finitely many. All generated frames for K4.3W must therefore be finite strict linear orderings, i.e. must be frames of the form

$$\underset{w_1}{\circ} \longrightarrow \ldots \longrightarrow \underset{w_n}{\circ}$$

for some natural number n, where no world is related to itself and each world is related to all later ones.

We are now ready to tackle the proof of non-compactness. Consider the (infinite) set of wff

(Λ) $\{Mp, MMp, \ldots, M^i p, \ldots\}$

i.e. the set of all wff of the form $M^n p$ where n is a natural number ≥ 1. We shall prove two things:

LEMMA 6.10
Λ is K4.3W-consistent.

LEMMA 6.11
Λ is not simultaneously satisfiable in any frame for K4.3W. Clearly the non-compactness of K4.3W follows immediately from these two lemmas.

PROOF OF LEMMA 6.10
Let A be any finite subset of Λ. Clearly A is a subset of some set of wff $A' = \{Mp, \ldots, M^n p\}$, which is itself a subset of Λ. Now consider a frame $\langle W, R \rangle$ which is a strict linear ordering with $n + 1$ worlds in W, i.e. the frame

$$\underset{w_0}{\circ} \longrightarrow \underset{w_1}{\circ} \longrightarrow \ldots \longrightarrow \underset{w_n}{\circ}$$

Clearly this is a frame for K4.3W. Let $\langle W, R, V \rangle$ be a model based on this frame in which $V(p, w) = 1$ for every $w \in W$. Then by $[VM^*]$ (p. 8), Mp is true at w_0 because p is true at w_1, MMp is true at w_0 because p is true at w_2, and in general, for each $i(1 \leq i \leq n)$, $M^i p$ is true at w_0 because p is true at w_i. Thus each wff in A' is true at w_0, which means that A' is simultaneously satisfiable in $\langle W, R \rangle$, and therefore that A' is K4.3W-consistent. Moreover, since A' is K4.3W-consistent, so clearly is A; and since A is any arbitrary finite subset of Λ, this means that Λ is K4.3W-consistent, which is what we had to prove.

PROOF OF LEMMA 6.11

Suppose that all the wff in Λ are true together at some world in a model $\langle W, R, V \rangle$ based on a frame for K4.3W. Then by Theorem 5.6 (p. 80), all these wff are true at w in the sub-model of $\langle W, R, V \rangle$ generated by w. Let this sub-model be $\langle W^*, R^*, V^* \rangle$. Then by Corollary 5.8, its frame $\langle W^*, R^* \rangle$, being a generated sub-frame of $\langle W, R \rangle$, must also be a frame for K4.3W. It must, therefore, as we showed above, be a finite strict linear ordering. It is, however, impossible for all the wff in Λ to be true at w (or indeed at any world) in such a frame, for this reason: W^* is finite; so let the number of worlds in it be n. This means that, since R^* is irreflexive and transitive, there are no worlds w and w' in W^* such that $wR^{*n}w'$. So, by $[VM^*]$ (p. 8), there is no $w \in W^*$ such that $V(M^n p, w) = 1$. But $M^n p \in \Lambda$; therefore Λ is not simultaneously satisfiable in any frame for K4.3W. This proves Lemma 6.11.

As we noted earlier, Lemmas 6.10 and 6.11 immediately yield

THEOREM 6.12
K4.3W is not compact.

A similar method, though involving a slightly more complicated set Λ, will yield a proof of the non-compactness of KW. (See Exercise 6.5, p. 110.)

A related system with a considerable independent interest of its own, which can also be shown to be non-compact, is one which is sometimes called S4.3.1.[9] This can be axiomatized as S4.3 with the addition of

N1 $L(L(p \supset Lp) \supset p) \supset (MLp \supset p)$

or its easily derived equivalent, which is sometimes easier to work with,

N1′ $L(\sim p \supset M(p . M \sim p)) \supset (MLp \supset p)$

This system has a long history, and was originally devised to axiomatize 'discrete linear time', i.e. to be the correct modal system if L means 'it is and always will be the case that', and the relation *is at least as early as* is taken to be not merely linear but also *discrete* in the sense that each moment (except the last, if there is one) has a unique immediate successor or 'next moment', with nothing between them. Here, however, we shall consider frames for S4.3.1 in general, without special regard to this particular interpretation. Any generated frame for S4.3.1 must of course be a frame for S4.3, and therefore must be weakly linear, i.e. reflexive, transitive and totally connected (see p. 82). In addition, in order to validate **N1**, it must consist of either (a) a single discrete linear sequence of worlds (with no proper clusters), or (b) a single cluster only, or (c) a single cluster preceded by a finite linear sequence of worlds. The reason is this: any weakly linear generated frame which is not of any of these kinds must either (i) contain at least one world preceded by a proper cluster, or else (ii) have infinitely many worlds between the generating world w and some other world w'. But in case (i) we can falsify **N1** by letting p be false at the generating world w and at some world in the cluster in question, and true at some other world in that cluster and everywhere else. And in case (ii) we can falsify **N1** by letting p be false at w and true at w' and at every subsequent world, and making value-assignments at the worlds between w and w' which ensure that each of them at which p is true is followed by one at which p is false, and each at which p is false is followed by one at which p is true.

   On the other hand, every weakly linear frame which satisfies either (a) or (b) or (c) does validate **N1**. This is easy to see in the case of (b); for the frame is then a frame for S5, and therefore the S5 theorem $MLp \supset p$, which is the consequent of **N1**, is valid on it. For (a) and (c) we argue as follows: we take the formula in the form **N1′**, since it is easier to work with here. To falsify this at a world w we must have both $L(\sim p \supset M(p . M \sim p))$ and MLp true, but p false, at w. For MLp to be true at w, there must be some later world w' such that p is true at it and at every point subsequent to it. In case (a), there can be only finitely many worlds between w and w', while in case (c) p must be true throughout the cluster at the end of the frame; so in either case there can be only a finite number of worlds at which p can be false, and these form a linear sequence. That being so, however, it is impossible for $L(\sim p \supset M(p . M \sim p))$ to be true at w. For what this formula means is that *every* world, from w onwards, at which p is false is followed by a world at which p is true but which is itself followed by one at which p is false again; and for this to hold in a linear sequence requires that p should be false at infinitely many distinct worlds.

The generated frames for S4.3.1 are therefore precisely the weakly linear frames which satisfy either (a) or (b) or (c).

We shall now outline a proof that S4.3.1 is not compact, leaving the reader to fill in the details from the fuller proof we gave for K4.3W. Let Λ be the set of wff $\{\alpha_0, \dots, \alpha_i, \dots\} \cup \{MLp\}$, where

$$\alpha_0 = p$$
$$\alpha_1 = M \sim p$$
$$\alpha_2 = M(\sim p \,.\, Mp)$$
$$\alpha_3 = M(\sim p \,.\, M(p \,.\, M \sim p))$$

and each α_{i+1}, where $i \geqslant 1$, is $M(\sim p \,.\, M(p \,.\, \alpha_{i-1}))$. We shall show that Λ is S4.3.1-consistent by showing that every finite subset of it is simultaneously satisfiable in some frame for S4.3.1. For take the set $\{\alpha_0, \dots, \alpha_n, MLp\}$ for any given (finite) n, and consider a linear frame $\langle \mathbf{W}, \mathbf{R} \rangle$ in which $\mathbf{W} = \{w_0, \dots, w_{n+1}\}$. This frame is clearly a frame for S4.3.1; and a model $\langle \mathbf{W}, \mathbf{R}, \mathbf{V} \rangle$ based on it, in which $\mathbf{V}(p, w_{n+1}) = 1$, and for every $w_i (0 \leqslant i \leqslant n)$, $\mathbf{V}(p, w_i) = 1$ or 0 according as i is even or odd, will make every wff in $\{\alpha_0, \dots, \alpha_n, MLp\}$ true at w_0.

On the other hand, Λ itself is not simultaneously satisfiable in any frame for S4.3.1. For as we saw in dealing with **N1**, in any model based on a generated frame for S4.3.1, in order that MLp should be true at a world w, p must be true at some later world w' and ever thereafter, and that leaves at most a finite linear sequence of worlds where p can be false anywhere. But for *all* the α_i s in Λ to be true at w in a linear sequence, that sequence must contain an infinite sequence of worlds at which p is alternately true and false. Thus Λ is not simultaneously satisfiable in any generated frame for S4.3.1, and therefore not in *any* frame for the system.

This shows that S4.3.1 is not compact, and therefore, of course, not canonical.[10]

Exercises – 6

6.1 Prove that every frame for the system D is serial.

6.2 Prove that every frame for $K + MLp \supset LMp$ is convergent (see p. 31).

6.3 Prove that $K + LMp \supset MLp$ provides the rule of disjunction.

6.4 Prove that the system K1.1 (see note 6 to this chapter) is not canonical. (Hint: use an amalgamation in which w^*Rw^*. Prove that K1.1 provides the rule of disjunction in the following form: where $\alpha_1, \ldots, \alpha_n$ are any wff and β is a wff of PC, then $\vdash L\alpha_1 \vee \ldots \vee L\alpha_n \vee \beta \rightarrow$ either $\vdash \alpha_i$ for some $i (1 \leqslant i \leqslant n)$ or $\vdash \beta$. Then show that the canonical model for K1.1 contains a pair of distinct worlds which can see each other, but that no frame for K1.1 contains such a pair.)

6.5 Prove that the system KW is not compact. (Hint: prove that every frame for KW must be irreflexive, transitive, and such that every world is related to some dead end in a finite number of steps. Then consider the set

$$\{Mp_1, L(p_1 \supset Mp_2), \ldots, L(p_i \supset Mp_{i+1}), \ldots\}$$

where $p_1, \ldots, p_i, \ldots$ are a denumerably infinite set of variables. Show, by adapting the methods used in the text, that this set is KW-consistent but not simultaneously satisfiable in any frame for KW.)
(The idea of using this set of wff was suggested to the authors by K. Fine.)

6.6 The system K3.1 is S4.3 + **J1** (see note 6 to this chapter). Use the set Λ defined on p. 109, but with the omission of MLp, to prove K3.1 is not compact.

Notes

1 The models we have discussed can be represented by an (irreflexive) *general* frame in which $P = \{W, \varnothing\}$ – i.e. the only allowable sets of worlds are W itself and the empty set. This general frame, however, is not a refined frame (i.e. a refined structure in Thomason's sense – see note 6, p. 67), since there is no $A \in P$ such that $w_1 \in A$ but $w_2 \notin A$. Although a general frame can be a frame for T without being reflexive, a refined frame will

be a frame for T only if it is reflexive. This fact may help to show the reason for introducing the notion of refined frames.

2 Lemmon and Scott (1977), pp. 44f.

3 A test similar to the one we give is found in Lemmon and Scott (1977), p. 45.

4 The formula **W** is called by that name in Segerberg (1971), p. 84. Boolos (1979) calls it **G**. Boolos, who discusses the system extensively, is interested in interpreting L as 'it is provable that'. Certain results obtained by Gödel (from whose name Boolos derives the name **G** for the formula) may be taken to mean that if you can prove of a proposition that it is true-if-provable, then you can prove the proposition itself; and that is what, with the intended interpretation of L, **W** (or **G**) says.

5 Our proof of this is in essentials the one given in Boolos (1979), p. 30. It is also proved in van Benthem (1979b), p. 71. Segerberg axiomatizes K W with the addition of **4**, and therefore calls it K4W.

6 This result (by a different method) was obtained in van Benthem (1979a), p. 5.

A system related to KW which is also non-canonical is one which Sobociński calls K1.1 (see *IML*, p. 266) and Segerberg (1971, p. 101) calls S4 Grz. Both these authors axiomatize this system as S4 +

> **J1** $L(L(p \supset Lp) \supset p) \supset p$

(though Segerberg, op. cit., p. 96, calls the formula **Grz**). K + **J1**, is, however, a sufficient axiomatization, since from this basis we can derive both **T** and **4** (see van Benthem and Blok (1978)). In K1.1, L might be thought of as meaning 'it is provable and true that'; cf. note 4 above, and chapter 13 of Boolos (1979). A proof that the system is not canonical is given in Hughes and Cresswell (1982). Note that there is no connection between the use of the letter 'K' in the name of this system and its use as a name for the minimal normal modal system.

7 Fine (1974a), p. 40. Note that S.K. Thomason (1972b) uses 'noncompactness' in a different sense.

8 Segerberg (1971). The system is first mentioned on p. 89; for its axioms see pp. 47, 51 and 84. **D1** and **D1**$_0$ are called **Lem** and **Lem**$_0$ respectively by Segerberg.

9 For S4.3.1 see *IML*, pp. 262f. and 289, and the references given there. In *IML*, following Prior, S4.3.1 was often also called D; but this use of 'D' has no connection with its use as a name for K + $Lp \supset Mp$.

10 Another proof that S4.3.1 is not canonical may be found in van Benthem (1980), p. 136 (where **N1** is referred to as **Dum**).

7 Subordination frames

In this chapter we shall explain and study a method of proving completeness which does not involve the use of canonical models, although it does use maximal consistent sets of formulae. This is in fact the method used in Part II of *IML*, and we shall call it the *subordination* method, since a key notion in it is that of a *subordinate* of a world in a frame. In *IML*, proofs obtained by this method were called *Henkin* proofs.

In proving completeness one might be interested in two rather different things. One might want to describe the class of *all* the frames for a certain system, and to prove that the system is characterized by this class. The canonical model method is probably the most efficient way of doing this, at least for those systems which are canonical. One might, however, also wish to show that the system in question is characterized by some narrower class of frames. We have in fact already obtained some results of this kind. For example, we proved in chapter 3 that K is characterized by the class of irreflexive frames (p. 49), and in chapter 5 (pp. 83–6), that S4.3 is characterized by the class of linear frames.

In proving these more restricted kinds of theorems, we typically used the canonical model for the system in question to prove that it was characterized by a wider class of frames than the class we had in mind, and then used techniques involving principles about generated frames, p-morphisms and the like to define a sub-class of this wider class which would, so to speak, do the same work. In fact most of the results which we shall prove in this chapter could also be proved in this way.[1]

The subordination method gives us a way of proving theorems of this latter kind directly, without going through the canonical model of the system in question. The main difference between the two methods is that when proving that a system S is complete by the canonical model method we use the syntactic properties of S to construct the frame of the model, and then show that it has the desired semantic characteristics; but in the subordination method we set out directly to construct a frame with the desired semantic characteristics. Another difference is that whereas the canonical model for S verifies every S-consistent wff without exception, no single model produced by the subordination method will do this, or make *only* the theorems of S valid in it. What we shall find instead (in successful cases) is that for each S-consistent set of wff there is *some* subordination model of the required kind which verifies every member of that set. But this, of course, is enough to prove completeness with respect to a given class of models; all that is required is that for each S-consistent wff there should be *some* verifying model in the class in question.

The subordination method is somewhat easier to apply to systems which contain D – i.e. which have $Lp \supset Mp$ (or its equivalent, $M(p \supset p)$) as a theorem – than to those which do not. We shall therefore assume to begin with that the systems we are dealing with contain D; we shall show how to modify the method to apply to other systems later on.

The canonical subordination frame

We start by defining a frame $\langle U, \Sigma \rangle$, which we shall call the *canonical subordination frame*.[2] The members of U (the 'worlds' in the frame) are all those sequences of numbers which consist *either* of the single number 0 *or* of 0 followed by a finite sequence of the natural numbers 1, 2, 3 .... Each $w \in U$, then, is such a sequence, and where *n* is any natural number, we write '*wn*' for the sequence formed by tacking *n* on at the end of *w*. We now define Σ by saying that for any *w* and $w' \in U$, $w \Sigma w'$ iff $w' = wn$ for some natural number *n*. We call Σ the *subordination* relation; where $w \Sigma w'$ we say that w' is a *subordinate* of w, and we call wn the nth subordinate of w.

The frame therefore consists of a world 0 which has a denumerable infinity of subordinates, each of which in turn has a denumerable infinity of its own subordinates, and so on indefinitely. It may be pictured with the help of this diagram:

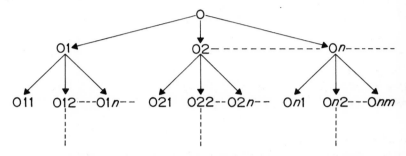

Next, having got our frame $\langle U, \Sigma \rangle$, we want to associate maximal consistent sets of wff with the worlds in it according to a certain plan. To be precise, if we are given a system S and an S-consistent set of wff Λ, we want to associate with each $w \in U$ a maximal S-consistent set Γ_w in such a way that

(1) $\Lambda \subseteq \Gamma_0$
(2) for any w, $w' \in U$, if $w \Sigma w'$ then $L^-(\Gamma_w) \subseteq \Gamma_{w'}$, (i.e., for any wff α, if $L\alpha \in \Gamma_w$, then $\alpha \in \Gamma_{w'}$); and
(3) for any $w \in U$, if $\sim L\alpha \in \Gamma_w$, then there is some $w' \in U$ such that $w \Sigma w'$ and $\sim \alpha \in \Gamma_{w'}$.

We want to be sure that this can always be done. Let us call a function Γ which satisfies these three requirements for a given Λ and S, an *S-maximality function for* Λ. Then what we need to prove is

THEOREM 7.1
If S is a normal modal system which contains D, and Λ is any S-consistent set of wff, then there exists an S-maximality function Γ for Λ.

PROOF
Since Λ is S-consistent, Theorem 2.2 (p. 19) assures us that there is a maximal S-consistent set which includes Λ. We next note that

since $\vdash_S Lp \supset Mp$, every maximal S-consistent set contains a denumerable infinity of wff of the form $M\alpha$, and therefore of wff of the form $\sim L\alpha$. We note, thirdly, that by Lemma 2.3 (p. 21) and Theorem 2.2, if an S-consistent set Δ contains a wff $\sim L\alpha$, then there is a maximal S-consistent set which contains $L^-(\Delta) \cup \{\sim \alpha\}$.

We now associate maximal S-consistent sets of wff with the worlds in U by induction in the following way:

With 0 we associate a maximal S-consistent set, Γ_0, which includes Λ. This ensures that Γ satisfies condition (1).

Then, given any $w \in U$ and the set Γ_w associated with it, we associate maximal S-consistent sets with its subordinates w_1, w_2, ... in this way: let the wff of the form $\sim L\alpha$ in Γ_w be enumerated in some order, let $\sim L\alpha_n$ be the nth of these, and let each Γ_{wn} be a maximal S-consistent set which includes $L^-(\Gamma_w) \cup \{\sim \alpha_n\}$. This ensures that Γ satisfies conditions (2) and (3).

This ends the proof.

It is worth noting that even when w and w' are distinct worlds in the canonical subordination frame, their associated sets of wff Γ_w and $\Gamma_{w'}$ may be identical. This contrasts with the position in a canonical model, where each world consists of a set of wff that is distinct from any of the others.

Proving completeness by the subordination method

Let us recall that what is meant by a system's being complete in the absolute sense explained in chapter 4 is that it is characterized by some class of frames. What this means is that there is a class $\mathscr{C}$ of frames for S such that every non-theorem of S fails in at least one of them: or, what comes to the same thing, such that every S-consistent wff is true in some world in some model based on some frame in $\mathscr{C}$. If we can prove that S is characterized by such a class of frames, then it of course follows that S is both sound and complete (in our earlier sense) with respect to $\mathscr{C}$, and also with respect to any other class of frames for S that includes $\mathscr{C}$.

Let us see in outline how we can use the canonical subordination frame to prove the completeness of D. We already know that every serial frame is a frame for D, and clearly the canonical subordination frame $\langle U, \Sigma \rangle$ is a serial frame. Now if we take an arbitrary D-consistent wff α, Theorem 7.1 assures us that there is a way of associating maximal D-consistent sets of wff with the worlds in this frame in such a way that α is in the set associated with the world 0 and the other conditions for a maximality function are also satisfied. We can then prove inductively – we shall show how to do so in a moment – that if we define a model $\langle U, \Sigma, V \rangle$ by letting each variable be true at any $w \in U$ iff it is in the set associated with w, then *every* wff will be true at any world iff it is in the set associated with that world. It will then follow that our D-consistent wff α is true at 0. So every D-consistent wff is true at some world in some model based on $\langle U, \Sigma \rangle$, and this shows that D is characterized by the single frame $\langle U, \Sigma \rangle$ itself (and of course by every class of frames for D of which $\langle U, \Sigma \rangle$ is a member).

For other systems we cannot proceed quite so simply. A frame for T, for example, must be reflexive, and one for S4 must be reflexive and transitive, but obviously $\langle U, \Sigma \rangle$ is neither reflexive nor transitive. What we do in such cases is to replace Σ by a relation R which

(a) is an extension of Σ, in the sense that it holds wherever Σ does;

(b) makes $\langle U, R \rangle$ a frame for the system S under consideration; and

(c) will enable us, when we form a model $\langle U, R, V \rangle$, using the V described in the previous paragraph, to carry through the inductive proof that any wff is true at any $w \in U$ iff it is in the set associated with w.

If we can define an R which meets these conditions, then it follows that S is characterized by the frame $\langle U, R \rangle$, by the same sort of argument which showed that D is characterized by $\langle U, \Sigma \rangle$ itself.

We shall now express all this more formally, and show how it can be proved.

By a *subordination frame* we shall mean a frame $\langle U, R \rangle$ in which U is the set of worlds in the canonical subordination frame $\langle U, \Sigma \rangle$ and R is an extension of Σ in the sense that for any w, $w' \in U$, if $w \Sigma w'$ then wRw'. (This includes the case where R is simply Σ itself.)

Given such a frame $\langle U, R \rangle$ and some maximality function Γ, we shall say that R *respects* Γ (and by extension that the frame itself respects Γ) iff, for all w, $w' \in U$, if wRw' then $L^-(\Gamma_w) \subseteq \Gamma_{w'}$. Note that since wherever $w\Sigma w'$ we have $L^-(\Gamma_w) \subseteq \Gamma_{w'}$ in any case, in order to show that R respects Γ we have only to show that $L^-(\Gamma_w) \subseteq \Gamma_{w'}$ in those cases where wRw' but not $w\Sigma w'$.

THEOREM 7.2

Let Γ be any maximality function with respect to a system S which contains D; let $\mathscr{F} (= \langle U, R \rangle)$ be a subordination frame which respects Γ; and let $(\mathscr{F}, V)$ be the model based on $\mathscr{F}$ in which, for every variable p, and every $w \in U$, $V(p, w) = 1$ iff $p \in \Gamma_w$. Then for every wff α and every $w \in U$, $V(\alpha, w) = 1$ iff $\alpha \in \Gamma_w$.

PROOF

The proof is by induction on the construction of a wff, and follows in essentials the lines of the proof of Theorem 2.4 (p. 23), to which the reader is invited to turn back. The inductions for $\sim$ and $\vee$ are straightforward, and are omitted here. The induction for L is as follows: we assume that the theorem holds for a wff α and show that in that case it holds for $L\alpha$.

(a) Suppose that $L\alpha \in \Gamma_w$. Now R respects Γ; i.e. $L^-(\Gamma_w) \subseteq \Gamma_{w'}$ for every w' such that wRw'. Hence $\alpha \in \Gamma_{w'}$ for every such w'. So by the induction hypothesis, $V(\alpha, w') = 1$ for every such w'. Hence by $[VL]$, $V(L\alpha, w) = 1$.

(b) Suppose that $L\alpha \notin \Gamma_w$. Then $\sim L\alpha \in \Gamma_w$. Hence by clause (3) in the definition of a maximality function, there is some $w' \in U$ such that $w\Sigma w'$ and $\sim \alpha \in \Gamma_{w'}$. Since R is an extension of Σ, we therefore have wRw'; and since $\sim \alpha \in \Gamma_{w'}$, we have $\alpha \notin \Gamma_{w'}$, and thus (by the induction hypothesis) $V(\alpha, w') = 0$. So by $[VL]$, $V(L\alpha, w) = 0$.

This ends the proof. Note that the fact that R respects Γ was needed only for step (a), and the fact that R is an extension of Σ only for step (b).

Theorems 7.1 and 7.2 now enable us to prove

THEOREM 7.3

Let S be a system which contains D. Then if $\mathscr{C}$ is a class of subordination frames each of which is a frame for S, and for every S-maximality function Γ there is some $\langle U, R \rangle \in \mathscr{C}$ which respects Γ, then S is characterized by $\mathscr{C}$ (and is therefore complete).

PROOF

Since each $\langle U, R \rangle \in \mathscr{C}$ is a frame for S (i.e. S is sound with respect to $\mathscr{C}$), it is sufficient to prove that every S-consistent wff is true at some world in some model based on some $\langle U, R \rangle \in \mathscr{C}$. Let β be any S-consistent wff. By Theorem 7.1 there is an S-maximality function Γ such that $\beta \in \Gamma_0$. By the hypothesis of the present theorem, there is some $\langle U, R \rangle \in \mathscr{C}$ which respects this Γ. Hence by Theorem 7.2 there is a model based on this $\langle U, R \rangle$ in which $V(\beta, 0) = 1$.

COROLLARY 7.4

If S is a system which contains D, and $\langle U, R \rangle$ is a subordination frame which is a frame for S and which respects every S-maximality function, then S is characterized by the single frame $\langle U, R \rangle$.

This is simply the special case of Theorem 7.3 in which we can define a single extension of $\langle U, \Sigma \rangle$ which respects every S-maximality function. For some systems we can do this, but for others we cannot. When we can, it is easier to use the corollary than the theorem in our proofs.

We have now filled in the missing steps in the completeness proof for D sketched on pp. 115f. As we noted there, the canonical subordination frame itself is a frame for D. If we then simply identify R with Σ, $\langle U, R \rangle$ will automatically respect every D-maximality function, since we shall have wRw' *only* when $w\Sigma w'$. Hence Corollary 7.4 shows that D is characterized by the single frame $\langle U, \Sigma \rangle$.

Tree frames

The canonical subordination frame is an example of what is often called a *tree frame* (or simply a *tree*). As we shall use this term, a tree frame is one which begins at a unique point, in which each point may branch outward to any number of other points (or to none), but in which there is no branching inward (or joining up) and no turning back. We define a tree frame, that is, as a frame $\langle W, R \rangle$ which is

(1) generated, in the sense explained on p. 78;
(2) antisymmetrical, in the sense that for no two distinct w and $w' \in W$ do we have both wRw' and $w'Rw$; and

(3) anticonvergent, in the sense that if w_1 and w_2 are distinct members of W and neither is related to the other, then for no $w_3 \in$ W which is distinct from each of them do we have both $w_1 R w_3$ and $w_2 R w_3$.

Note that there is nothing in this definition either to forbid or to require that a tree frame should be either reflexive or transitive – or even serial, since it may or not contain dead ends. By a *reflexive tree* we shall simply mean a tree frame in which R is reflexive, and so forth. A tree frame cannot, however, be symmetrical, except in the trivial case in which it consists of a single element only. The canonical subordination frame is a tree which has the special features of being irreflexive, intransitive and serial, and in which each point is related to infinitely many others.

As we remarked earlier, if a system S is characterized by a class of frames $\mathscr{C}$, it is also characterized by any class of frames for S which includes $\mathscr{C}$. Hence, since every serial frame is a frame for D, our proof that $\langle U, \Sigma \rangle$ characterizes D also establishes

THEOREM 7.5
D is characterized by (a) the class of all irreflexive serial frames ; (b) the class of all intransitive serial frames ; (c) the class of all serial trees.

THEOREM 7.6
T is characterized by the class of all reflexive trees.

PROOF
We define a subordination frame $\langle U, R \rangle$ by letting wRw' iff either $w \Sigma w'$ or $w = w'$. Obviously R is an extension of Σ. Obviously, too, R is reflexive over U, and therefore $\langle U, R \rangle$ is a frame for T. We now prove that R respects every T-maximality function Γ. The only cases in which we have wRw' but not $w \Sigma w'$ are those in which $w = w'$. So all we have to prove is that $L^-(\Gamma_w) \subseteq \Gamma_w$, i.e. that whenever we have $L\alpha \in \Gamma_w$ we also have $\alpha \in \Gamma_w$. And this follows immediately, by Lemma 2.1e (p. 19), from the fact that Γ_w is a maximal T-consistent set and $\vdash_T L\alpha \supset \alpha$.

Thus by Corollary 7.4, T is characterized by the single frame $\langle U, R \rangle$. It is clear that this is a reflexive tree. Hence, since every reflexive frame is a frame for T, T is characterized by the class of all reflexive trees.

Theorem 7.6 should be compared with Theorems 2.9 (p. 28) and 6.1 (p. 90). The former of these (together with the soundness of T) amounts to a proof that T is characterized by the class of all reflexive frames, and the latter shows that these are all the frames for T that there are; so between them they show that T is characterized by the class of all frames for T. That result also follows from Theorem 7.6, but we now have the additional result that T is characterized by a certain proper sub-class of all the frames for the system. For many reflexive frames are not trees: e.g.

Since every tree frame is antisymmetrical (though not vice versa), we also have

COROLLARY 7.7
T is characterized by the class of all reflexive antisymmetrical frames.

This is also a result we have not obtained before, since not every reflexive frame is antisymmetrical.

THEOREM 7.8
S4 is characterized by the class of all reflexive transitive trees.

PROOF
Let $\langle U, R \rangle$ be the frame obtained from the canonical subordination frame $\langle U, \Sigma \rangle$ by defining R as the smallest relation such that, for any w_1, w_2 and $w_3 \in U$

(1) if $w_1 = w_2$ then $w_1 R w_2$; and
(2) if $w_1 R w_2$ and $w_2 \Sigma w_3$, then $w_1 R w_3$.

R, thus defined, is an extension of Σ. For suppose that $w\Sigma w'$: by (1) we have wRw; so we have both wRw and $w\Sigma w'$; hence by (2) we have wRw'. $\langle U, R \rangle$ is therefore a subordination frame. It is also easy to see that R is both reflexive and transitive, and that the frame is therefore a frame for S4. Moreover, it clearly remains a tree.

We now prove that R respects any S4-maximality function Γ. The only cases where we have wRw' but not $w\Sigma w'$ are (i) where $w = w'$, and (ii) where $w\Sigma^n w'$ for some $n > 1$. For (i) the proof is as for T, since S4 contains T. For (ii), suppose that $L\alpha \in \Gamma_w$. Then since $\vdash_{\mathrm{S4}} L\alpha \supset L^n\alpha$ (for any $n > 1$), we have $L^n\alpha \in \Gamma_w$. Hence, since $w\Sigma^n w'$, we have $\alpha \in \Gamma_{w'}$.

Thus by Corollary 7.4, S4 is characterized by the single frame $\langle U, R \rangle$. Since this is a reflexive transitive tree, and every such tree is a frame for S4, the theorem follows.

A relation which is reflexive, transitive and antisymmetrical (as R is in all reflexive transitive trees) is called a *partial ordering*; and if R is a partial ordering over W, we call the frame $\langle W, R \rangle$ a partial ordering as well. The class of all partial orderings is intermediate between that of all reflexive transitive frames on the one hand, and that of all reflexive transitive trees on the other. A partial ordering precludes proper clusters in the sense explained on pp. 82f., but it allows 'branching inward', which trees do not. Thus the frame

is reflexive and transitive but is not a partial ordering; and the frame

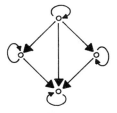

is a partial ordering but not a tree. All trees, however, are partial orderings; so, since every partial ordering, being both reflexive and transitive, is a frame for S4, Theorem 7.7 gives us

COROLLARY 7.9
S4 is characterized by the class of all partial orderings.

We now consider the system B. A frame for B must be reflexive and symmetrical, and we can define such a frame $\langle U, R \rangle$ by letting $w\mathrm{R}w'$ iff either $w = w'$ or $w\Sigma w'$ or $w'\Sigma w$.

THEOREM 7.10
B is characterized by the single frame $\langle U, R \rangle$ defined above.

We leave the details of the proof to the reader. The only new step is to show that when $w\Sigma w'$, $L^-(\Gamma_{w'}) \subseteq \Gamma_w$, and this can be done as follows: since $w\Sigma w'$, we have $L^-(\Gamma_w) \subseteq \Gamma_{w'}$, and hence by Theorem 2.6 (p. 25) we have $M^+(\Gamma_{w'}) \subseteq \Gamma_w$. Now suppose $L\alpha \in \Gamma_{w'}$. Then $ML\alpha \in \Gamma_w$. Hence since $\vdash_{\mathbf{B}} ML\alpha \supset \alpha$, we have $\alpha \in \Gamma_w$.

This is a fresh result, since the only single frame we have hitherto found which characterizes **B** is the frame of its canonical model, and that is certainly not the same as our present $\langle \mathbf{U}, \mathbf{R} \rangle$. For one thing, $\langle \mathbf{U}, \mathbf{R} \rangle$ contains only denumerably many worlds, whereas the frame of the canonical model contains non-denumerably many.

As we have defined a tree, the $\langle \mathbf{U}, \mathbf{R} \rangle$ of Theorem 7.10 is not a tree, since it is not antisymmetrical. It is, however, very like a tree frame in that if we were to visualize it along the lines of the diagram on p. 114, all we should have to do would be to think of each world as related to itself and each arrow as being double-headed. To put this more precisely: let us say that a frame $\langle \mathbf{W}, \mathbf{R}^* \rangle$ is the *reflexive symmetrical extension* of a frame $\langle \mathbf{W}, \mathbf{R} \rangle$ iff, for every w and $w' \in \mathbf{W}$, $w\mathbf{R}^*w'$ iff either $w = w'$ or $w\mathbf{R}w'$ or $w'\mathbf{R}w$. Then the $\langle \mathbf{U}, \mathbf{R} \rangle$ of Theorem 7.10, though not itself in the strict sense a tree, is the reflexive symmetrical extension of the tree $\langle \mathbf{U}, \Sigma \rangle$. Since the reflexive symmetrical extension of any frame is obviously itself reflexive and symmetrical, and therefore a frame for **B**, we have

COROLLARY 7.11
B is characterized by the class of the reflexive symmetrical extensions of all tree frames.

Another feature of the $\langle \mathbf{U}, \mathbf{R} \rangle$ of Theorem 7.10 is that it contains no sub-frame consisting of three or more distinct worlds each of which is related to all the others. **B** is therefore also characterized by the class of all reflexive symmetrical frames which satisfy this condition. A consequence of this is that in falsifying any non-theorem of **B** we never need to use a frame in which there are three or more worlds each of which can see all the others.

We turn to S5. $Lp \supset p$, $Lp \supset LLp$ and $MLp \supset p$ are all theorems of S5; and by using the relevant steps in the proofs for T, S4 and **B**, we can easily prove

THEOREM 7.12
S5 *is characterized by the single frame* $\langle U, R \rangle$ *in which* wRw′ *for all* w, w′ ∈ U.

We leave the proof to the reader. The crucial point is that any world in $\langle U, \Sigma \rangle$ can be reached from any other world in a finite number of forward or backward Σ-steps.

If in a frame $\langle W, R \rangle$ we have wRw′ for all w, w′ ∈ W, then R is said to be a *universal* relation (over W). Now so long as R is universal over U, the nature of the worlds in U, and the order in which they are arranged, is irrelevant to the evaluation of formulae, and only the number of the worlds matters. Hence we have

COROLLARY 7.13
S5 is characterized by any frame $\langle W, R \rangle$ in which W is a denumerably infinite set and R is universal over W.

S5 is, of course, characterized by the frame of its canonical model. But R is not universal in that frame, since, as we saw on pp. 95f., it is split up into a number of disjoint sub-frames. Corollary 7.13 is therefore also a result we have not obtained before.[3]

S4.3 and linearity

In chapter 5 (pp. 83–6) we proved that S4.3 is characterized by the class of all linear frames. In this section we shall show how to prove the same result by the subordination method, without going through the canonical model or using principles about generated frames or the bulldozing technique. What we shall do is to take the canonical subordination frame $\langle U, \Sigma \rangle$ and show how, given any S4.3-maximality function Γ, we can define over U a linear relation R which is an extension of Σ and respects Γ. Since R is linear, $\langle U, R \rangle$ will in each case be a frame for S4.3, and so by Theorem 7.3, S4.3 will be characterized by the class of all such frames.

We begin by noting that U has only a denumerable infinity of members. These can therefore be enumerated, i.e. put into 1–1 correspondence with the natural numbers. Furthermore, they can be enumerated in such a way that any wn – i.e. any w′ such that wΣw′ – occurs later in the enumeration than w. (There are several ways in which this can be done, one of which is this: where w is the sequence $\langle a_1, ..., a_n \rangle$, let $p_1, ..., p_n$ be the first n prime numbers, let $\bar{w}$ be $p_1^{a_1} \times ... \times p_n^{a_n}$, and let the ws be enumerated in the order of magnitude of the corresponding $\bar{w}$s.) Let us also use the notation '$L(\Lambda)$' for the set of all wff of the form $L\alpha$ in a given set Λ; i.e.

$$L(\Lambda) = \{L\alpha : L\alpha \in \Lambda\}$$

Now suppose that we have some S4.3-maximality function Γ. We shall show that the following definition of R satisfies the conditions we have mentioned:

For any w and $w' \in U$, wRw' iff $L(\Gamma_w) \subseteq L(\Gamma_{w'})$ and in addition *either*

(i) $w = w'$

or

(ii) $L(\Gamma_{w'}) \nsubseteq L(\Gamma_w)$

or

(iii) w precedes w' in the enumeration.

What we have to show about R, so defined, is that it is an extension of Σ, that it respects Γ, and that it is a linear relation (i.e. reflexive, transitive, totally connected and antisymmetrical).

LEMMA 7.14
R is an extension of Σ.

PROOF
Suppose that $w\Sigma w'$. Consider any wff $L\alpha \in \Gamma_w$. Since S4.3 contains S4, we then have $LL\alpha \in \Gamma_w$, and therefore $L\alpha \in \Gamma_{w'}$. So $L(\Gamma_w) \subseteq L(\Gamma_{w'})$. Moreover, since $w\Sigma w'$, w precedes w' in the enumeration, so condition (iii) in the definition of R holds. Thus we have wRw'.

LEMMA 7.15
R respects Γ.

PROOF
Suppose that wRw'. We have to show that $L^-(\Gamma_w) \subseteq \Gamma_{w'}$. So consider any wff $L\alpha \in \Gamma_w$. Since wRw', $L(\Gamma_w) \subseteq L(\Gamma_{w'})$, so $L\alpha \in \Gamma_{w'}$; hence, since S4.3 contains T, we have $\alpha \in \Gamma_{w'}$ as required.

LEMMA 7.16
R is reflexive.

PROOF
Obviously, if $w = w'$, $L(\Gamma_w) \subseteq L(\Gamma_{w'})$ and condition (i) is satisfied.
So wRw'.

LEMMA 7.17
R is transitive.

PROOF
Suppose that (a) $w_1 R w_2$ and (b) $w_2 R w_3$. We have to prove that $w_1 R w_3$. We note first that since $L(\Gamma_{w_1}) \subseteq L(\Gamma_{w_2})$ and $L(\Gamma_{w_2}) \subseteq L(\Gamma_{w_3})$, we have $L(\Gamma_{w_1}) \subseteq L(\Gamma_{w_3})$.

Next, as far as condition (i) is concerned, it is trivial (for *any* definition of R) that if $w_1 R w_2$ and $w_2 R w_3$, and either $w_1 = w_2$ or $w_2 = w_3$, then $w_1 R w_3$. So it remains only to consider the cases in which (a) and (b) satisfy either condition (ii) or condition (iii).

(1) Suppose that R in (a) satisfies condition (ii). Then since $L(\Gamma_{w_2}) \not\subseteq L(\Gamma_{w_1})$, there is some wff $L\beta \in \Gamma_{w_2}$ which is not in Γ_{w_1}. But since $L(\Gamma_{w_2}) \subseteq L(\Gamma_{w_3})$, $L\beta$ is also in Γ_{w_3}, and so $L(\Gamma_{w_3}) \not\subseteq L(\Gamma_{w_1})$. Hence we have $w_1 R w_3$ by condition (ii).

(2) Suppose now that R in (a) satisfies condition (iii). Then if R in (b) also satisfies condition (iii), we have both w_1 preceding w_2 and w_2 preceding w_3 in the enumeration, and so w_1 preceding w_3; therefore we have $w_1 R w_3$ by condition (iii). And if R in (b) satisfies condition (ii), there is some $L\beta \in \Gamma_{w_3}$ which is not in Γ_{w_2}; but then, since $L(\Gamma_{w_1}) \subseteq L(\Gamma_{w_2})$, $L\beta \notin \Gamma_{w_1}$; so $L(\Gamma_{w_3}) \not\subseteq L(\Gamma_{w_1})$, and so again we have $w_1 R w_3$, by condition (ii).

LEMMA 7.18
For any w and $w' \in U$, either $L(\Gamma_w) \subseteq L(\Gamma_{w'})$ or $L(\Gamma_{w'}) \subseteq L(\Gamma_w)$.

PROOF
We note first that since R is a reflexive transitive extension of Σ, we have $0Rw$ for every $w \in U$. Now suppose that for some w and $w' \in U$, neither $L(\Gamma_w) \subseteq L(\Gamma_{w'})$ nor $L(\Gamma_{w'}) \subseteq L(\Gamma_w)$. Then there is some $L\beta \in \Gamma_w$ such that $\sim L\beta \in \Gamma_{w'}$, and also some $L\gamma \in \Gamma_{w'}$ such that $\sim L\gamma \in \Gamma_w$; and as a result, $L\beta \supset L\gamma \notin \Gamma_w$ and $L\gamma \supset L\beta \notin \Gamma_{w'}$. But since $0Rw$ and $0Rw'$, and R respects Γ, neither $L(L\beta \supset L\gamma)$ nor $L(L\gamma \supset L\beta)$ is in Γ_0. But this is impossible, since $\vdash_{S4.3}$

$L(L\beta \supset L\gamma) \lor L(L\gamma \supset L\beta)$. (The proof is by substituting $L\beta$ for p and $L\gamma$ for q in D1, and replacing LL by L by the S4 rule. Note that this is the only point at which we use the S4.3 axiom **D1**.)

LEMMA 7.19
R is totally connected.

PROOF
We have to prove that for any w and $w' \in U$, if not wRw' then $w'Rw$.

Suppose that not wRw'. Then by the definition of R, either (a) $L(\Gamma_w) \nsubseteq L(\Gamma_{w'})$, or (b) none of conditions (i)–(iii) hold for wRw'. In case (a), we have $L(\Gamma_{w'}) \subseteq L(\Gamma_w)$ by Lemma 7.18; so we have both $L(\Gamma_{w'}) \subseteq L(\Gamma_w)$ and $L(\Gamma_w) \nsubseteq L(\Gamma_{w'})$, and therefore $w'Rw$ by condition (ii). In case (b), by the failure of condition (ii) we have $L(\Gamma_{w'}) \subseteq L(\Gamma_w)$. Moreover, by the failure of condition (iii), either $w = w'$ or w' precedes w in the enumeration. Hence we have $w'Rw$ either by condition (i) or by condition (iii). So in either case we have $w'Rw$.

LEMMA 7.20
R is antisymmetrical.

PROOF
Suppose that for some w and $w' \in U$, both wRw' and $w'Rw$. Then by the first clause in the definition of R, both $L(\Gamma_w) \subseteq L(\Gamma_{w'})$ and $L(\Gamma_{w'}) \subseteq L(\Gamma_w)$. Hence condition (ii) in the second clause cannot be satisfied either by wRw' or by $w'Rw$. Moreover, condition (iii) cannot be satisfied by *both* of them, since then we should have both w preceding w' and w' preceding w, which is clearly impossible. Therefore condition (i) must be satisfied by one of them, and so we have $w = w'$. Thus R is antisymmetrical.

THEOREM 7.21
S4.3 *is characterized by the class of all linear frames.*[4]

PROOF
Lemmas 7.15–7.20 have shown that for any S4.3-maximality function Γ there is a linear frame $\langle U, R \rangle$ which respects Γ. By Lemma 7.14, R is an extension of Σ, and therefore $\langle U, R \rangle$ is a subordination frame. Since every linear frame is a frame for S4.3, the theorem then follows by Theorem 7.3.

Systems not containing D

We shall now see how to apply the subordination method to normal modal systems that do not contain D. These include K, K4, B4, MV and Ver. One complication with these systems arises from the fact that if S does not contain D, then the set of *all* wff of the form $L\alpha$ is S-consistent. We might as well prove this before we go any farther. Suppose, then, that for some normal modal system S, the set of all wff of the form $L\alpha$ is S-inconsistent. This means that for some wff $L\alpha_1, \ldots, L\alpha_n$,

$$\vdash_S \sim (L\alpha_1 \ldots . L\alpha_n)$$

So by *L*-distribution,

$$\vdash \sim L(\alpha_1 \ldots . \alpha_n)$$

But $\vdash_K \sim L\beta \supset M(p \supset p)$ (for any wff β)

So by MP,

$$\vdash_S M(p \supset p)$$

– which means that S contains D. So if S does not contain D, the set of all wff of the form $L\alpha$ is S-consistent.

This means, of course, that if S does not contain D, then some maximal S-consistent sets will contain all wff of the form $L\alpha$, and therefore none at all of the form $\sim L\alpha$. Now we proved in Lemma 2.13 (p. 34) that in any model, if $V(L(p . \sim p), w) = 1$ then w is a dead end. And this means that, in a model constructed in accordance with Theorem 7.2, any maximal consistent set which contains all wff of the form $L\alpha$, would have to be associated with a dead end. In fact, the possibility that a frame for S should contain dead ends is precisely correlated with Ss not containing D. Every frame for any system that contains D must be a serial frame – i.e. it must have no dead ends in it; but if S does not contain D, then at least some of the frames for S *will* contain dead ends.

Unfortunately for our present purposes, the canonical subordination frame $\langle U, \Sigma \rangle$ contains no dead ends, and it is clear that no frame $\langle U, R \rangle$ in which R is an extension of Σ can contain any either. So we cannot use the canonical subordination frame as it stands to prove completeness for systems that do not contain D.

We shall deal with this complication in the following way. Instead of having only a single canonical subordination frame, we shall have a whole class of them; one of these will be the canonical subordination frame as we originally defined it, and the others will be what we shall call *truncated* canonical subordination frames. A truncated canonical subordination frame is exactly like our original canonical subordination frame except that Σ stops at one or more $w \in U$, in the sense that such a w is not Σ-related to any worlds in U at all. In other words it is one which is formed from our original $\langle U, \Sigma \rangle$ by deleting all the worlds below one or more of the worlds in U – i.e. every $w' \in U$ such that for some n, $w\Sigma^n w'$. Our revised definition of a canonical subordination frame (which can easily be seen to cover the old one) will therefore be: $\langle U, \Sigma \rangle$ is a canonical subordination frame iff (A) U is a set of sequences of numbers satisfying the following conditions:

(1) $0 \in U$;

(2) where Nat is the set of natural numbers 1, 2, 3, ... , if $w \in U$, then either $wn \in U$ for every $n \in$ Nat, or else $wn \notin U$ for any $n \in$ Nat;

and (B) for any $w, w' \in U$, $w\Sigma w'$ iff $w' = wn$ for some $n \in$ Nat.

If for some $w \in U$ there is no $wn \in U$, we shall say that w is a *dead end* in $\langle U, \Sigma \rangle$.

We shall now indicate the modifications we need to make in our earlier treatment to free it from the restriction to systems that contain D.

A maximality function can be defined exactly as on p. 114, though we have to remember that $\langle U, \Sigma \rangle$ can now be a canonical subordination frame which has dead ends.

In Theorem 7.1 we omit the phrase 'which contains D', so that the theorem now is

THEOREM 7.1′

If S is any normal modal system and Λ is any S-consistent set of wff, then there exists an S-maximality function Γ for Λ on some canonical subordination frame.

The proof will now run: since Λ is S-consistent, Theorem 2.2 assures us that there is a maximal S-consistent set containing Λ. Let Γ_0 be such a set. Then Γ satisfies condition (1). Next, if we are given Γ_w for some $w \in U$, there are two possibilities: either (i) Γ_w

contains no wff of the form $\sim L\alpha$, or (ii) it contains a denumerable infinity of such wff. If (i) holds, let $\langle U, \Sigma \rangle$ be a canonical subordination frame in which w is a dead end. If (ii) holds, let $\langle U, \Sigma \rangle$ be a frame in which w is not a dead end, and let $\sim L\alpha_n$ be the nth wff of the form $\sim L\alpha$ in Γ_w. By Lemma 2.3 and Theorem 2.2, there is a maximal S-consistent set which includes $L^-(\Gamma_w) \cup \{\sim \alpha_n\}$. Let Γ_{wn} be such a set, for each n. Then in each case there is some $\langle U, \Sigma \rangle$ for which Γ also satisfies conditions (2) and (3).

What Theorem 7.1' means is that if Λ is any S-consistent set of wff, then there is *some* canonical subordination frame on which we can impose a pattern of maximal S-consistent sets, associating a set containing Λ with the initial world 0, and other sets with the other worlds in the frame in a way that satisfies conditions (2) and (3) in the definition of a maximality function. A maximality function Γ can conveniently, if somewhat informally, be thought of as such a pattern of maximal consistent sets. Now it should be clear from the proof of Theorem 7.1' that which canonical subordination frame we are led to is determined by the particular Γ under consideration. For it is Γ that determines with which worlds we are to associate maximal consistent sets containing no wff of the form $\sim L\alpha$, and thus which worlds are to be dead ends; and this is the only way in which one canonical subordination frame differs from another. It is therefore convenient to be able to index canonical subordination frames with reference to the maximality functions that determine them; and we shall write '$\langle U, \Sigma \rangle_\Gamma$' to denote the canonical subordination frame determined by Γ in the way just described. Sometimes we shall want to refer to the class of all canonical subordination frames determined by any S-maximality function, for some normal system S. We shall call this, for brevity, the class of *canonical subordination frames determined by S*.

Given two frames $\langle W, R_1 \rangle$ and $\langle W, R_2 \rangle$, based on the same W, we say that $\langle W, R_1 \rangle$ is an *extension* of $\langle W, R_2 \rangle$ iff, for every $w, w' \in W$, if wR_2w' then wR_1w'. We can then extend our previous notion of a subordination frame to include any extension $\langle U, R \rangle$ of any canonical subordination frame $\langle U, \Sigma \rangle$.

The definition of 'R respects Γ' on p. 117 needs no modification. The new form of Theorem 7.2 is

THEOREM 7.2′

Let Γ be any maximality function with respect to any normal modal system S; let $\mathscr{F}(= \langle U, R \rangle)$ be an extension of $\langle U, \Sigma \rangle_\Gamma$ in which R respects Γ; and let $\langle \mathscr{F}, V \rangle$ be the model based on $\mathscr{F}$ in which for every variable p and every $w \in U$, $V(p, w) = 1$ iff $p \in \Gamma_w$. Then for every wff α and every $w \in U$, $V(\alpha, w) = 1$ iff $\alpha \in \Gamma_w$.

This can be proved in the same way that Theorem 7.2 was.

In place of Theorem 7.3 we have

THEOREM 7.3′

Let S be any normal modal system. Suppose that $\mathscr{C}$ is a class of subordination frames, each of which is a frame for S, and that for every S-maximality function Γ there is in $\mathscr{C}$ some extension of $\langle U, \Sigma \rangle_\Gamma$ which respects Γ. Then S is characterized by $\mathscr{C}$ (and is therefore complete).

PROOF

Since every frame in $\mathscr{C}$ is a frame for S (i.e. S is sound with respect to $\mathscr{C}$), it is sufficient to prove that every S-consistent wff is true at some world in some model based on some $\langle U, R \rangle \in \mathscr{C}$. Let β be any S-consistent wff. By Theorem 7.1′, there is some S-maximality function such that for the canonical subordination frame $\langle U, \Sigma \rangle_\Gamma$, $\beta \in \Gamma_0$. By the hypothesis of the present theorem, $\mathscr{C}$ contains some frame $\langle U, R \rangle$ which is an extension of $\langle U, \Sigma \rangle_\Gamma$ and which respects Γ. Hence by Theorem 7.2′, there is a model based on $\langle U, R \rangle$ in which $V(\beta, 0) = 1$.

As before, we have a corollary which is simpler though of more limited application:

COROLLARY 7.4′

If S is any normal modal system, and every canonical subordination frame determined by S is a frame for S, then S is characterized by the class of all those frames.

This is an immediate consequence of Theorem 7.3′, since obviously Σ is an extension of itself and Σ respects every maximality function.

THEOREM 7.22

K is characterized by (a) the class of all trees, and (b) the class of all antisymmetrical frames.

PROOF

Since *every* frame is a frame for K, every canonical subordination frame determined by K is a frame for K. Hence by Corollary 7.4′, K is determined by the class of those frames. But each of these is a tree, and every tree is antisymmetrical.

We turn now to K4 (i.e. $K + Lp \supset LLp$). We already know that every transitive frame is a frame for K4.

Given any frame $\langle W, R \rangle$, we say that $\langle W, R^+ \rangle$ is the *transitive extension* of $\langle W, R \rangle$ iff R^+ is the least relation over W such that (i) if wRw' then wR^+w', and (ii) if $w_1 R^+ w_2$ and $w_2 R w_3$, then $w_1 R^+ w_3$. It should be clear that the transitive extension of any frame is a transitive frame.

On p. 121 we defined a *partial ordering* as a relation (or a frame) that is reflexive, transitive and antisymmetrical. A relation (or a frame) that is transitive and *irreflexive* is known as a *strict partial ordering*.

THEOREM 7.23

K4 is characterized by (a) the class of all transitive trees, and (b) the class of all strict partial orderings.

PROOF

Let $\mathscr{C}$ be the class of the transitive extensions of all the canonical subordination frames determined by K4. Since every frame in $\mathscr{C}$ is transitive, every frame in $\mathscr{C}$ is a frame for K4. Moreover, for each canonical subordination frame $\langle U, \Sigma \rangle$ determined by K4 there will be some $\langle U, R \rangle \in \mathscr{C}$ in which R is an extension of Σ. We now show that each such R respects every K4-maximality function Γ. The only cases to be considered are those in which we have wRw' and $w\Sigma^n w'$ for $n > 1$. Since $\vdash_{K4} L\alpha \supset L^n\alpha$ for any $n > 1$, we have $L^-(\Gamma_w) \subseteq \Gamma_{w'}$ as in the proof of Theorem 7.8.

Thus by Theorem 7.3′, K4 is characterized by $\mathscr{C}$. Now every transitive extension of a canonical subordination frame is both a transitive tree and also a strict partial ordering, and all such frames, being transitive, are frames for K4. Therefore K4 is characterized by each of the classes of frames mentioned.

We can deal similarly with KB (i.e. $K + \sim p \supset L \sim Lp$). We know that every symmetrical frame is a frame for KB. Given any canonical subordination frame $\langle U, \Sigma \rangle$, we say that $\langle U, R \rangle$ is the *symmetrical extension* of $\langle U, \Sigma \rangle$ iff for any $w, w' \in U$, wRw' iff either $w\Sigma w'$ or $w'\Sigma w$. This will make R symmetrical and irreflexive. $\langle U, R \rangle$, of course, will not be a tree (except in the trivial case in which 0 is the only member of U). We leave it to the reader to prove

THEOREM 7.24
KB is characterized by (a) the class of all symmetrical extensions of canonical subordination frames, and (b) the class of all irreflexive symmetrical frames.

For Ver and MV we can obtain no new results of interest; nevertheless we shall sketch briefly how the subordination method deals with these systems.

Since every wff of the form $L\alpha$ is a theorem of Ver, every maximal Ver-consistent set will contain all such wff, and hence none of the form $\sim L\alpha$. Thus every Ver-maximality function will force us to make 0 a dead end, and so the only canonical subordination frame determined by Ver is the single-world frame $\langle \{0\}, \varnothing \rangle$ – i.e. the frame in which 0 is the only member of U, and Σ is the empty relation, and therefore is irreflexive. We already know (p. 34) that every one-world irreflexive frame is a frame for Ver. Therefore by Corollary 7.4', Ver is characterized by the single frame $\langle \{0\}, \varnothing \rangle$, and hence by any one-membered irreflexive frame.

This is of course the same result as we obtained by the canonical model method in chapter 2. We also proved there that the system MV, which can be axiomatized as K +

MV' $\quad LMp \supset Lq,$

is characterized by the class of all frames in which every world either is a dead end or can see some dead end. We can prove a slightly stronger result by our present methods.

THEOREM 7.25
MV is characterized by the class of all tree frames in which every world either is a dead end or is related to some dead end.

PROOF
We already know that every frame in which every world either is or is related to a dead end is a frame for MV. We now show that

every canonical subordination frame determined by **MV** is of this kind. Transposition and substitution in the axiom **MV'** show that for any wff α,

$$\vdash_{\text{MV}} \sim L\alpha \supset \sim LM \sim (p . \sim p)$$

It follows that every maximal **MV**-consistent set of wff will either contain no wff of the form $\sim L\alpha$, or else (if it contains even one such) will contain $\sim LM \sim (p . \sim p)$. Hence if Γ is any **MV**-maximality function, in the canonical subordination frame $\langle U, \Sigma \rangle_\Gamma$, every Γ_w will either (i) contain no wff of the form $\sim L\alpha$, or (ii) contain $\sim LM \sim (p . \sim p)$. In case (i) w will be a dead end in $\langle U, \Sigma \rangle_\Gamma$. In case (ii), there will be some subordinate of w, say wi, such that $\sim M \sim (p . \sim p) \in \Gamma_{wi}$, and therefore $L(p . \sim p) \in \Gamma_{wi}$. Since $\vdash L(p . \sim p) \supset L\alpha$ for any wff α (in any normal system), we then have $L\alpha \in \Gamma_{wi}$ for every wff α. So Γ_{wi} contains no wff of the form $\sim L\alpha$, and wi is thus a dead end in $\langle U, \Sigma \rangle_\Gamma$; that is, w is Σ-related to some dead end.

By Corollary 7.4', therefore, **MV** is characterized by the class of all canonical subordination frames in which every world either is a dead end or is related to some dead end. Since every canonical subordination frame is a tree, the theorem follows.

Exercises – 7

7.1 Prove that D + $Lp \supset LLp$ is characterized by the single frame $\langle W, R \rangle$ in which W = U and wRw' iff $w\Sigma^n w'$ for some $n > 0$.

7.2 Prove that K + $LL(p . \sim p)$ is characterized by the truncated canonical subordination frame in which all the subordinates of 0 are dead ends.

7.3 Prove that there is a single tree frame which characterizes K.

7.4 Prove that K + $Mp \equiv Lp$ is characterized by the single frame $\langle W, R \rangle$ in which W is the set of all natural numbers and nRm iff $n + 1 = m$.

7.5 Prove that D + $Mp \supset LMp$ is characterized by the single frame $\langle W, R \rangle$ in which W = U and R is defined so that wRw' iff

   (i) $w = 0$ and $w\Sigma w'$

or

(ii) $w \neq 0$ and $w' \neq 0$

(Hint: first prove that $M^n Lp \supset L^m p$ is a theorem of this system for any n and $m \geqslant 1$.)

7.6 Prove that $S4 + MLp \supset (p \supset Lp)$ is characterized by the single frame $\langle W, R \rangle$ in which W is the set of all natural numbers and $n R m$ iff $n = m = 0$ or $m > 0$.

7.7 Prove that KBE (i.e. $K + p \supset LMp + Mp \supset LMp$) is characterized by the following pair of frames: (1) the frame $\langle W, R \rangle$ in which W is the set of all natural numbers and $n R m$ for every n and m; and (2) the frame $\langle \{0\}, \varnothing \rangle$ (i.e. the frame in which the only member of W is 0 and it is a dead end).

Notes
1 See, e.g., chapter 2 of Segerberg (1971) and Sahlqvist (1975), pp. 128–32. A method closer to our own may be found in Schumm (1972). Some of the results can also be obtained by the method of semantic diagrams given in Part I of *IML*.
2 The terminology of this section essentially follows Hughes and Cresswell (1975), pp. 24f., except that the letter Σ is used for subordination rather than S. This avoids confusion with the use of S as a metavariable for modal systems.
3 This corollary still holds when 'denumerably' is omitted, though we have not proved that here.
4 It should be noted that this theorem does not exhibit any particular linear frame which characterizes S4.3. Some results in this area are known. For instance, if W is either the rational numbers or the real numbers and R is $\leqslant$ then $\langle W, R \rangle$ characterizes S4.3. If, however, W is natural numbers then a stronger system (S4.3.1) is characterized. A full study of just what sorts of linear structures determine what sorts of modal systems is found in Segerberg (1970). Segerberg gives bibliographical references for all results he derives from other authors.

8 Finite models

The finite model property

We saw on p. 25 that every normal modal system is characterized by a single model; that is to say, for every normal modal system S there is some model such that the wff that are valid in that model are precisely the theorems of S. The canonical model for S, for example, is always such a model. Canonical models are, of course, infinite, in the sense that in each of them W has infinitely many members; and indeed no consistent modal system has the property of being characterized by a single finite model (though some, such as the Trivial system and the Verum system, are characterized by a single finite *frame*).

There is, however, a related property which is possessed by a great many modal systems, including all of the most familiar ones, and that is the property of being characterized by a class of models each one of which is finite. This property is known as the *finite model property*. Another way of expressing the fact that a system S has this property is by saying that every non-theorem of S fails at some world in some finite model for S. (A model for S, of course, is simply a model in which every theorem of S is valid.) We can give a precise definition as follows:

If S is a normal modal system, then S *has the finite model property* iff, for every wff α which is not a theorem of S, there is a model $\langle$ W, R, V $\rangle$ in which W is finite and

(i) there is some $w \in W$ such that $V(\alpha, w) = 0$;
(ii) if β is a theorem of S, then for every $w \in W$, $V(\beta, w) = 1$.

There is an intimate connection between a system's possessing the finite model property and its being *decidable*, in that, as we shall show later in this chapter, every modal system which has the finite model property and is finitely axiomatizable in the sense explained on p. 6, is decidable: that is to say, there is an effective procedure for determining, of any given wff α, in a finite number of steps, whether it is or is not a theorem of S.

Filtrations

The most efficient and widely applicable known method of proving that a system has the finite model property is that of *filtrations*,[1] which we shall now describe.

Briefly, the idea behind the method is this. We know that, although not every normal modal system is characterized by a class of frames, every such system is characterized by some class of models. This means that if α is any non-theorem of S, then α is invalid in some model $\langle W, R, V \rangle$ which is a model for S. The model in question may, of course be an infinite one. But what the method enables us to do is to use $\langle W, R, V \rangle$ to produce another model $\langle W^*, R^*, V^* \rangle$ in which α is also invalid but in which W^* is finite, and which, in successful cases, is also a model for S. Clearly, if we can show how to do this for any arbitrary non-theorem of S, we thereby show that S has the finite model property.

We shall now explain the details of the method.

First, consider any wff α of modal logic. Let Φ_α be the set of all sub-formulae (well-formed parts) of α, when α is expressed in terms of primitive operators only. For example, $\Phi_{Lp \supset q}$ is

$$\{p, q, Lp, \sim Lp, \sim Lp \vee q\}$$

Since every wff is of finite length, Φ_α is always finite. It also has the property of being *closed under sub-formulae*. What this means is that if $\beta \in \Phi_\alpha$ and γ is a sub-formula of β, then $\gamma \in \Phi_\alpha$. Of course, even infinite sets of wff can be closed under sub-formulae, and in fact when we come to state the fundamental theorem for filtrations (Theorem 8.1), we shall state it for any set of wff, finite or infinite, which is closed under sub-formulae. But the application of this theorem to proving that a system has the finite model property will rely on the fact that, for any wff α, there are only finitely many wff in Φ_α.

Next, we recall that on pp. 75f. we introduced the notions of equivalent worlds, and of equivalence classes of worlds, in a model. We shall now relativize these notions, and the notation we used for them, to a given set of wff. That is, given a model $\langle$ W, R, V $\rangle$ and a set of wff Φ, we shall say that w and w' are equivalent worlds (that $w \approx w'$) with respect to $\langle$ W, R, V $\rangle$ and Φ iff, for every wff β in Φ, if β is true in w then it is true in w', and if β is false in w then it is false in w', no matter how w and w' may differ in other respects. We shall say that a subset of W is the equivalence class of w (in W) iff it consists of all and only those worlds in W which are equivalent to w, again with respect to Φ; we use the notation '[w]' for this equivalence class, usually leaving it to the context to make clear the relativity to a particular Φ. And we shall say that a subset A of W is an equivalence class in W with respect to Φ iff there is some $w \in$ W such that A $= [w]$ with respect to Φ. What this amounts to is that there is some subset Λ of Φ such that the members of A are precisely those worlds in which every wff in Λ is true and every other wff in Φ is false. Thus we can give the following formal definition:

Given a model $\langle$ W, R, V $\rangle$ and a set of wff Φ, a subset A of W is an *equivalence class in W with respect to* Φ iff A is non-empty and there is some subset Λ of Φ such that, for every $w \in$ W, $w \in$ A iff, for every $\beta \in \Lambda$, $V(\beta, w) = 1$ and for every $\gamma \in \Phi$-Λ, $V(\gamma, w) = 0$.

Note that if Φ is finite, this means that for each equivalence class A there will be a unique wff δ, viz.

$$\beta_1 . \dots . \beta_j . \sim \gamma_1 . \dots . \sim \gamma_k$$

where $\{\beta_1, \dots, \beta_j\} = \Lambda$ and $\{\gamma_1, \dots, \gamma_k\} = \Phi$-$\Lambda$, such that any $w \in$ W is in A iff δ is true in w. We shall call δ the *characteristic* Φ-*formula* for A.

It is not hard to see that for any $\langle$ W, R, V $\rangle$ and Φ, each $w \in$ W belongs to one and only one equivalence class with respect to Φ, and that if $w \approx w'$, then w and w' belong to the same equivalence class. W, therefore, splits up into a number of disjoint equivalence classes with respect to Φ. Moreover, if Φ is finite (as Φ_α is for any wff α), the number of such equivalence classes will also be finite, since there are only a finite number of ways of assigning truth-values to a finite number of formulae.

Although the worlds in an equivalence class with respect to Φ may be differentiated from one another by the fact that many wff may be true in some of them but false in others, the important point for our present purposes is that there is no wff in Φ which so distinguishes them. As far as Φ is concerned, we could take any world in such an equivalence class as doing duty for all the rest. This is the basic idea behind the method of filtrations.

The next step is to define a filtration. Suppose that we have a model $\langle W, R, V \rangle$ and a set of wff Φ which is closed under subformulae. Then a *filtration of* $\langle W, R, V \rangle$ *through* Φ is any model $\langle W^*, R^*, V^* \rangle$ which satisfies the following conditions:

(1) W^* is a subset of W which consists of exactly one world from each equivalence class with respect to Φ. In other words, for every $w \in W$, there is exactly one $w' \in W^*$ such that $w \approx w'$.[2]

Note that if Φ is finite, so is W^*, but that if Φ is infinite, W^* may also be infinite but it may not.

(2) V^* is defined simply as the original V, restricted to the members of W^*. That is, for any variable p and any $w \in W^*$,

$$V^*(p, w) = V(p, w)$$

(3) The requirements for R^* are somewhat more complicated. For $\langle W^*, R^*, V^* \rangle$ to count as a filtration of $\langle W, R, V \rangle$ through Φ, R^* can be any relation over W^* which is, as we shall say, *suitable*; and R^* is suitable iff it satisfies both of the following conditions:

(i) For any w and $w' \in W^*$, if there is some $u \in W$ such that wRu and $w' \approx u$, then wR^*w'.

(ii) For any w and $w' \in W^*$, if wR^*w', then, for every wff $L\beta \in \Phi$, if $V(L\beta, w) = 1$, $V(\beta, w') = 1$.

It may help in understanding these two conditions if we think of them as expressing minimum and maximum conditions, respectively, for the suitability of R^*. Suppose we visualize models, in our usual way, with the accessibility relations represented by arrows. Then condition (i) means that if in the original model $\langle W, R, V \rangle$ there was an arrow from w to *any* world in $[w']$ – even if there was not one from w to w' itself – then we *must* have an arrow from w to w' in our new model $\langle W^*, R^*, V^* \rangle$; otherwise it will not be a filtration of $\langle W, R, V \rangle$ through Φ. Condition (ii) means that we are *allowed* to insert other arrows as well, but only provided that we do not transgress the limits set by (ii); we must not, that is, insert any extra arrows from a w to a w' in our new model if in the old model there was any wff $L\beta$ in Φ which was true at w while β itself was false at w'. But any R^* which keeps within these limits counts as suitable.

We can now state and prove the fundamental theorem for filtrations:

THEOREM 8.1
Suppose that $\langle W, R, V \rangle$ is any model, that Φ is any set of wff which is closed under sub-formulae, and that $\langle W^*, R^*, V^* \rangle$ is any filtration of $\langle W, R, V \rangle$ through Φ. Then for every wff $\beta \in \Phi$ and every $w \in W^*$, $V^*(\beta, w) = V(\beta, w)$.

PROOF
The proof is by induction on the construction of a modal wff. If β is a variable, the theorem holds by the definition of V^* in a filtration. The inductions for the truth-functors are straightforward and we shall omit them. The induction for L is as follows: given that a wff $L\gamma$ (and therefore γ too) is in Φ, we take as our induction hypothesis that the theorem holds for γ, and show that in that case it also holds for $L\gamma$. We shall do this by proving that $V(L\gamma, w) = 0$ iff $V^*(L\gamma, w) = 0$.

(a) Suppose that $V^*(L\gamma, w) = 0$, for some $w \in W^*$. Then by $[VL]$, $V^*(\gamma, w') = 0$ for some $w' \in W^*$ such that wR^*w'. So by the induction hypothesis, $V(\gamma, w') = 0$. But R^* is suitable; hence by condition (ii), $V(L\gamma, w) = 0$.

(b) Suppose now that $V(L\gamma, w) = 0$, for some $w \in W^*$. Clearly $w \in W$, and so by $[VL]$ we have $V(\gamma, u) = 0$ for some $u \in W$ such that wRu. Now by the definition of W^*, there will be some $w' \in W^*$ such that $w' \approx u$; so by condition (i) for R^*, we have wR^*w'. Furthermore, since $V(\gamma, u) = 0$, $w' \approx u$, and $\gamma \in \Phi$, we also have $V(\gamma, w') = 0$. So by the induction hypothesis, $V^*(\gamma, w') = 0$. Therefore by $[VL]$, since wR^*w', $V^*(L\gamma, w) = 0$.

This completes the proof of Theorem 8.1.

We can now easily prove

THEOREM 8.2
Suppose that a wff α is invalid in a model $\langle W, R, V \rangle$. Then α is invalid in every filtration of $\langle W, R, V \rangle$ through Φ_α.

PROOF
Since α is invalid in $\langle W, R, V \rangle$, there is some $w \in W$ such that $V(\alpha, w) = 0$. Suppose that $\langle W^*, R^*, V^* \rangle$ is a filtration of $\langle W, R, V \rangle$ through Φ_α. By the definition of W^*, there is some $w^* \in W^*$ such that $w \approx w^*$ with respect to $\langle W, R, V \rangle$ and Φ_α. Obviously, $\alpha \in \Phi_\alpha$; therefore $V(\alpha, w^*) = 0$. Hence by Theorem 8.1, $V^*(\alpha, w^*) = 0$, and so α is invalid in $\langle W^*, R^*, V^* \rangle$, which is what we had to prove.

These theorems, as we have stated them, do not assume that we always can form a filtration of any given model through any given Φ. However, a little reflection will show that we always can. All that we need to be assured of is that, for any $\langle W, R, V \rangle$ and Φ, some suitable R^* can be defined; for the choice of the members of W^* from the equivalence classes in W is arbitrary, and once it is made, V^* is fixed. And there are always ways in which this can be done. The two simplest ways are by strengthening either condition (i) or condition (ii) for the suitability of R^* to an 'if and only if' condition. It should be clear that we can always satisfy each of these strengthened conditions on its own; and that either of these courses would result in satisfying *both* of the original conditions follows immediately from the fact that the converse of (i) entails (ii) and the converse of (ii) entails (i). We can prove this as follows:

Suppose that the converse of (i) holds; i.e. that whenever wR^*w', there is some $u \in W$ such that wRu and $w' \approx u$. We want to show that, in that case, if $L\beta$ is in Φ and is true at w in the original model, then β is true at w' in the original model. Now we do not necessarily have wRw', but at least we have wRu. Hence by [VL], β is true at u. But Φ is closed under sub-formulae, and therefore, since $L\beta$ is in Φ, so is β. So, since $w' \approx u$, if β is true at u it is also true at w'.

Suppose now that the converse of (ii) holds; i.e. that if, in the original model, whenever $L\beta$ is in Φ and is true at w, β is true at w', then in the new model we have wR^*w'. We want to prove that, in that case, if in the original model there is some

$u \in W$ such that wRu and $w' \approx u$, then in the new model we have $wR*w'$. Suppose, then, that there is some such u. Then by [VL], for every wff $L\beta$ which is true at w, and hence in particular for every wff $L\beta \in \Phi$ which is true at w, β is true at u. Therefore, since $\beta \in \Phi$ and $w' \approx u$, β is also true at w'. Hence by the converse of (ii) we have $wR*w'$.

The importance of this is that one way of ensuring that $R*$ is suitable, which is always open to us, is by making both (i) and its converse hold, and another way, which is also always open to us, is by making both (ii) and its converse hold. These yield what, following Segerberg, we might call, respectively, the *finest* and the *coarsest* filtrations of $\langle W, R, V \rangle$ through Φ.[3]

Proving that a system has the finite model property

In this section we shall explain and illustrate how to use filtrations to prove that a system has the finite model property.

Let us survey the position we have reached so far. Suppose that S is any normal modal system. By Corollary 2.5 (p. 25), we know that if α is any arbitrary non-theorem of S, then α is invalid in some model $\langle W, R, V \rangle$ which is a model for S. We also know that there exists at least one filtration, $\langle W*, R*, V* \rangle$, of $\langle W, R, V \rangle$ through Φ_α, and that in every such filtration $W*$ is finite. Theorem 8.2 then assures us that α is invalid in $\langle W*, R*, V* \rangle$, and thus that it is invalid in some finite model.

For *every* normal system S, then, every non-theorem of S is invalid in some finite model. Does this mean that every normal system has the finite model property? No, it does not, for this reason: for a system S to have the finite model property, every non-theorem of S must be invalid, not merely in some finite model or other, but in some finite model *which is a model for S*; and we have not yet proved *that* about any system. Certainly we have shown that if we start from a model for S in which a wff α is invalid, we can always form one or more finite models (filtrations of that model through Φ_α) in which α is also invalid; but what we have *not* shown is that any of the models we thus end up with is itself a model *for S*.

To show, for a particular system S, that every model in a class which characterizes S has a filtration which is itself a model for S, is a non-trivial task since, as we shall see later on in this chapter, there are normal systems which do not have the finite model property. What it means for S to lack the finite model property is that there is some wff α which is not a theorem of S, and yet that no finite model in which it is invalid is a model for S. There will, of course, be models for S in which α is invalid, but these will all be infinite ones; and this means that, since any filtration through Φ_α is finite, that no filtration of any of these models through Φ_α will be a model for S at all.

For most of the systems we have discussed, however, it is not hard to prove that this kind of situation cannot arise, and therefore that they do have the finite model property. The easiest way to do this for a particular system S is by taking a class of models which characterizes S – and then showing that for each of these models there is some filtration (through any given Φ) whose *frame* is a frame for S. Typically, the way we show this is by establishing that R^* in the filtration in question satisfies some condition which is known to be sufficient to make the frame a frame for S. We may not, indeed, be able to prove that *every* filtration of a given model has an R^* which does this; but, as we have seen, it will be sufficient to prove that at least one of its filtrations does. For some systems, however, we can prove the stronger claim that they are characterized by a class of models where R^* satisfies the relevant condition in every such filtration. This happens, for example, with K and T.

THEOREM 8.3
K has the finite model property.

PROOF
For the proof of this theorem we have merely to observe that, since every frame is a frame for K, every filtration of any model will be based on a frame for K.

THEOREM 8.4
T has the finite model property.

PROOF
Since T is characterized by the class of all reflexive models, it is sufficient to prove that every filtration $\langle W^*, R^*, V^* \rangle$ of a reflexive model $\langle W, R, V \rangle$ is itself reflexive. To prove this, consider any $w \in W^*$. Clearly $w \approx w$; and we are given that

wRw. Hence there is some $w' \in$ W, namely w itself, such that wRw' and $w' \approx w$. Therefore we have wR*w by condition (i) for the suitability of R*; and this is what we had to prove.

We turn now to S4. As we know, S4 is characterized by the class of all models which are reflexive and transitive. We cannot in fact prove that every filtration of a reflexive and transitive model is itself reflexive and transitive. However, as we have observed, it is not necessary to prove this in order to show that S4 has the finite model property. It is sufficient to prove that for every model for S4 there is some filtration of it (through any given Φ) which is reflexive and transitive; and this we can prove.

THEOREM 8.5

S4 has the finite model property.

PROOF

Let $\langle$ W, R, V $\rangle$ be any model for S4 and let Φ be any set of wff closed under sub-formulae. To prove the theorem, it is sufficient to show that there is some filtration of $\langle$ W, R, V $\rangle$ through Φ which is reflexive and transitive.

Let $\langle$ W*, R*, V* $\rangle$ be a model in which W* and V* are as previously defined for a filtration of $\langle$ W, R, V $\rangle$ through Φ, and R* is defined as follows:

For any w and $w' \in$ W*, wR*w' iff, for every wff

$L\beta \in \Phi$, if V($L\beta, w$) = 1 then V($L\beta, w'$) = 1.

It is obvious that R*, as so defined, is reflexive and transitive. To show that $\langle$ W*, R*, V* $\rangle$ is a filtration of $\langle$ W, R, V $\rangle$ through Φ, and thus to prove the theorem, it is sufficient to prove that R* is suitable. We do this as follows:

(a) To show that R* satisfies condition (i) for suitability, suppose that for some $u \in$ W, wRu and $w' \approx u$. Let $L\beta$ be a wff in Φ such that V($L\beta, w$) = 1. Then by S4, V($LL\beta, w$) = 1. Hence by [VL], since wRu, V($L\beta, u$) = 1. But $w' \approx u$, and $L\beta \in \Phi$, so V($L\beta, w'$) = 1. Hence by the definition of R* we have wRw*, as required by condition (i).

(b) To show that R* satisfies condition (ii), suppose that wR*w' and that V($L\beta, w$) = 1 (where $L\beta \in \Phi$). Then by the definition of R*, V($L\beta, w'$) = 1. Hence, since S4 contains T, we have V(β, w') = 1, as required by condition (ii).

Thus R^* is suitable, and so $\langle W^*, R^*, V^* \rangle$ is a filtration of $\langle W, R, V \rangle$ through Φ.

This completes the proof.

The key step in the proof we have just given was the devising of an appropriate R^* – that is, an R^* which would both be suitable, so that the resulting model would be a filtration, and also have the required semantic properties (in this case, reflexiveness and transitivity). By defining analogous R^*s we can prove that many other systems have the finite model property. There is no fixed recipe for doing this, and imagination may be needed; but we have in effect reduced the problem of proving that a system has the finite model property to that of finding the right kind of R^*.

In the proof of Theorem 8.5 we had, near the end, to appeal to the fact that S4 contains T. The proof did not, therefore, show that every model for K4 (which does not contain T) has a filtration which is even transitive; and thus it did not give us a finite model property result for K4, which is characterized by the class of all transitive models. Nevertheless we can obtain this result by a very similar proof, by using the following definition of R^*:

For any w and $w' \in W^*$, wR^*w iff, for every wff $L\beta \in \Phi$,

if $V(L\beta, w) = 1$ then both $V(L\beta, w') = 1$ and $V(\beta, w') = 1$.

We leave the reader to fill in the details.

THEOREM 8.6
B has the finite model property.

PROOF
Since B is characterized by the class of all reflexive and symmetrical models, it is sufficient to show that if $\langle W, R, V \rangle$ is any such model and Φ is any set of wff closed under sub-formulae, we can define an R^* which is reflexive and symmetrical and also suitable. Let R^* be defined as follows:

For any w and $w' \in W^*$, wR^*w' iff, for every wff $L\beta \in \Phi$,

both (a) if $V(L\beta, w) = 1$ then $V(\beta, w') = 1$, and (b) if

$V(L\beta, w') = 1$ then $V(\beta, w) = 1$.

The symmetry of R^* follows immediately from this definition. As we showed in the proof of Theorem 8.4, R^* is reflexive in all filtrations of reflexive models. So all that remains to be proved is that R^* is suitable.

To show that R^* satisfies condition (i) for suitability, suppose that there is some $u \in W$ such that wRu and $w' \approx u$. Then for any wff $L\beta \in \Phi$, if $V(L\beta, w) = 1$, then $V(\beta, u) = 1$; and hence, since Φ is closed under sub-formulae, $V(\beta, w') = 1$. Thus condition (a) in the definition of R^* holds. Moreover, since R is symmetrical, we also have uRw. Then since $w' \approx u$, if $V(L\beta, w') = 1$, $V(L\beta, u) = 1$; and since uRw, we have $V(\beta, w) = 1$. Thus condition (b) in the definition of R^* also holds. So by that definition we have wR^*w', as required by condition (i).

That R^* satisfies condition (ii) for suitability follows immediately from its definition.

This completes the proof of Theorem 8.6.

THEOREM 8.7
S5 has the finite model property.

PROOF
The proof follows the same lines as before. We recall that S5 is characterized by the class of all models in which R is an equivalence relation. We use the following definition of R^*:

For any w and $w' \in W^*$, wR^*w' iff, for every wff

$L\beta \in \Phi$, $V(L\beta, w) = V(L\beta, w')$.

It should be clear that R^*, as thus defined, is an equivalence relation. The proof of its suitability should now be straightforward, and we leave it to the reader.

Filtration proofs that many other systems have the finite model property will be found in the literature of the subject.[4]

The completeness of KW
In the previous sections we have used the filtration technique to prove that various systems which we had already shown to be complete have the finite model property. In this section we shall show how to use it in order to establish a completeness result itself. The system we shall consider is the system KW, which we discussed on pp. 100–3 and which we axiomatized

as K +

W $L(Lp \supset p) \supset Lp$

One of the things we proved about KW is that it contains $Lp \supset LLp$ as a theorem, and is therefore an extension of K4. (It does not, however, contain $Lp \supset p$, and so is not an extension of S4.) We also stated, but did not prove, that it is characterized by the class of all strict finite partial orderings – i.e. by the class of all models $\langle W, R, V \rangle$ in which W is finite and R is transitive and irreflexive. Soundness is not hard to prove: all one has to do is to show that **W** cannot be falsified in any model of the kind described, and that is a quite straightforward task. Our aim is now to prove completeness.[5]

It should be clear that for this purpose our usual method of canonical models would be ineffectual; for, as we proved in chapter 5, the canonical model for KW is not irreflexive, and therefore does not belong to the class of models with respect to which we want to prove that KW is complete. We can, however, use the filtration method instead.

We begin by proving two preliminary lemmas.

LEMMA 8.8

If a wff β is KW-consistent, so is $L \sim \beta . \beta$.

PROOF

Suppose that $L \sim \beta . \beta$ is not KW-consistent. Then (1) $\vdash_{KW} L \sim \beta \supset \sim \beta$. Hence by N, $\vdash_{KW} L(L \sim \beta \supset \sim \beta)$, and so by **W**, $\vdash_{KW} L \sim \beta$. But this and (1) give us, by MP, $\vdash_{KW} \sim \beta$, which means that β is not KW-consistent. This proves the lemma.

If A is any set of worlds in a model $\langle W, R, V \rangle$, let us say, following Segerberg,[6] that a world w in A is *final* in A iff it cannot see any world in A (not even itself). Our other lemma then is

LEMMA 8.9

Let $\langle W, R, V \rangle$ be the canonical model for KW, and let A be any equivalence class in W with respect to some finite set of wff Φ. Then there is some world $w^* \in A$ which is final in A.

PROOF

Since Φ is finite, let δ be the characteristic Φ-formula for A, as defined on p. 137. Since every equivalence class in W is non-empty, δ must be consistent. Hence by Lemma 8.8, $L \sim \delta . \delta$ is also consistent; so there must be some $w^* \in W$ such that $L \sim \delta . \delta \in w^*$. By the fundamental theorem for canonical models (Theorem 2.4, p. 23), we therefore have both (i) $V(L \sim \delta, w^*) = 1$ and (ii) $V(\delta, w^*) = 1$. By (ii), we then have $w^* \in A$. And by (i), any world that w^* can see must contain $\sim \delta$. and so not be in A. Thus w^* is final in A, which proves the lemma.

THEOREM 8.10

If α is valid in every finite transitive irreflexive model, then $\vdash_{KW} \alpha$. (I.e. KW is complete with respect to the class of all such models.)

PROOF

We prove the theorem by assuming that a wff α is not a theorem of KW and proving that in that case it is invalid in some finite transitive irreflexive model.

Since $\nvdash_{KW} \alpha$, α is invalid in the canonical model for KW, $\langle W, R, V \rangle$. Let $\langle W^*, R^*, V^* \rangle$ be the following model:

W^* consists of precisely one final world in each equivalence class in W with respect to Φ_α. (Lemma 8.9 assures us that there is always such a final world.) Clearly W^* is finite and satisfies the condition for W^* in a filtration of $\langle W, R, V \rangle$ through Φ_α.

For any w and $w' \in W^*$, wR^*w' iff (a) $w \neq w'$ and (b) for every wff $L\beta \in \Phi_\alpha$, if $V(L\beta, w) = 1$ then both $V(L\beta, w') = 1$ and $V(\beta, w') = 1$. (It is obvious that R^* is irreflexive and transitive.)

V^* is defined as for a filtration.

To show that $\langle W^*, R^*, V^* \rangle$ is a filtration of $\langle W, R, V \rangle$ through Φ_α, we need only show that R^* is suitable. It is obvious that it satisfies condition (ii) for suitability. To show that it also satisfies condition (i), suppose that for some w and $w' \in W^*$ there is some $u \in W$ such that both wRu and $w' \approx u$. Then since w is a final world in $[w]$, u cannot be in $[w]$; therefore neither can w', and so w' cannot be w itself. Thus clause (a) in the definition of R^* holds. Next, let $L\beta$ be any wff in Φ_α such that $V(L\beta, w) = 1$. Then since KW contains K4, we have $V(LL\beta, w) = 1$. Hence, since wRu, we have both $V(\beta, u) = 1$ and $V(L\beta, u) = 1$. But $w' \approx u$, and both β and $L\beta$ are in Φ_α. Therefore we have both $V(\beta, w') = 1$ and $V(L\beta, w') = 1$. So clause (b) in the definition of R^* also holds, and therefore, by that definition, we have wR^*w' as required by condition (i) for suitability.

Thus $\langle W^*, R^*, V^* \rangle$ is a filtration of $\langle W, R, V \rangle$ through Φ_α. Therefore by Theorem 8.2, α is invalid in $\langle W^*, R^*, V^* \rangle$; and, as we have seen, this model is finite, transitive and irreflexive.

This proves Theorem 8.10.

Characterization by classes of finite models

If a normal modal system has the finite model property, this means that it is characterized by some class of finite models. But any system may be characterized by many different classes of models; and the fact that a system has the finite model property does *not* mean that whenever it is characterized by a class $\mathscr{C}$ of models, it is also characterized by the class of all finite models in $\mathscr{C}$. A trivial proof of this lies in the fact that if $\mathscr{C}$ is the class whose only member is the canonical model for a system S, then S is characterized by $\mathscr{C}$; in this case, however, there are *no* finite models in $\mathscr{C}$, and therefore (provided that S is a consistent system) S is not characterized by the (empty) class of all the finite models in $\mathscr{C}$.

Other cases, however, are less trivial. For example, we proved in chapter 7 (see Theorem 7.8, p. 120) that S4 is characterized by the class of all models based on reflexive transitive trees. Moreover, we have proved in this chapter that S4 has the finite model property. But S4 is not characterized by the class of all finite models based on reflexive transitive trees.[7] We can prove this as follows: let $\langle W, R, V \rangle$ be any such model. Then since W is finite and $\langle W, R \rangle$ is a reflexive transitive tree, every $w \in W$ can see some world which can see itself but only itself. Now if w' is any world of this kind, then any wff $L\alpha$ must have the same value at w' as α itself has. So, since either p is true at w' or $\sim p$ is true at w', we must have

$$V(Lp \vee L \sim p, w') = 1$$

for every such w'. And therefore, since every $w \in W$ can see some such w', we have

$$V(M(Lp \vee L \sim p), w) = 1$$

for every $w \in W$. This means that $M(Lp \vee L \sim p)$ is valid in every finite model based on any reflexive transitive tree. It is not,

however, a theorem of S4. For the frame

$$w_1 \qquad w_2$$

is reflexive and transitive, and is therefore a frame for S4; but $M(Lp \vee L \sim p)$ fails in any model based on it in which $V(p, w_1) \neq V(p, w_2)$.

The same moral can be drawn from S4.3. This system is characterized by the class of all weakly linear models, as we showed in chapter 5, on pp. 83f. Moreover, it is not difficult to prove that it is also characterized by the class of all finite weakly linear models.[8] (The proof of this is left as an exercise.) In addition, as we also showed, on pp. 84–6, S4.3 is characterized by the class of all linear models. However, it is not characterized by the class of all finite linear models; for the formula $M(Lp \vee L \sim p)$ discussed above is valid in all such models, but is not a theorem of S4.3 since it can easily be falsified on a reflexive, transitive and connected frame.

A third example is K4. As we observed on p. 144, K4 has the finite model property. Moreover, we proved in chapter 7 (Theorem 7.23, p. 131) that K4 is characterized by the class of all strict partial orderings. We have, however, just proved that the system which is characterized by the class of all *finite* strict partial orderings is KW; and that KW is stronger than K4 may be seen from the fact that W fails on the (transitive) frame which consists of one world which is related to itself.

In summary, if we know that S has the finite model property, then if 𝒞 is the class of *all* models for S, we can be sure that S is characterized by the class of all the finite models in 𝒞; but if 𝒞 is some other class of models which characterizes S, then S may be characterized by the class of all the finite models in 𝒞, but it may not.

The finite frame property

At the beginning of this chapter we defined the finite model property as the property of being characterized by a class of finite models. Analogously, we can introduce the term 'finite frame property' for the property of being characterized by a class of finite frames. The formal definition, set out in the style used for that of the finite model property, will be this:

If S is a normal modal system, then S *has the finite frame property* iff, for every wff α which is not a theorem of S, there is a frame $\mathscr{F}$ ($= \langle$ W, R $\rangle$) in which W is finite and

(i) There is some model based on $\mathscr{F}$ in which, for some $w \in$ W, $V(\alpha, w) = 0$.

(ii) Every theorem of S is valid on $\mathscr{F}$.

As we saw in chapter 4, although every normal modal system is characterized by some class of models, not every normal modal system is characterized by some class of frames. This might lead us to expect that some systems might have the finite model property but not the finite frame property. Nevertheless, it turns out that this is not so, and that every system which has one of these properties also has the other. It is, in fact, an obvious and trivial result that if S has the finite frame property, then it has the finite model property; for if S is characterized by a certain class of frames, it is also characterized by the class of all models based on those frames. What is not either obvious or trivial is the converse result, which is due to Segerberg,[9] that if S has the finite model property, then it also has the finite frame property. We shall now show how to prove this.

We first recall the definition of a *distinguishable* model which was given on p. 75. This was to the effect that a model $\langle$ W, R, V $\rangle$ is distinguishable iff, for any w and $w' \in$ W, if $w \neq w'$ then there is some wff α such that $V(\alpha, w) \neq V(\alpha, w')$. (Clearly every filtration is a distinguishable model.) We proved in Theorem 5.5 (p. 76) that for any model whatsoever there is a distinguishable model which is equivalent to it in the sense of validating exactly the same formulae, and moreover that this distinguishable model contains no more worlds than the original model does. This means that every finite model is equivalent to some finite distinguishable model, and, therefore that if a system has the finite model property, it is characterized by a class of distinguishable finite models. The result that every system which has the finite model property also has the finite frame property will then follow as a corollary of Theorem 8.12 below. As a preliminary to proving this theorem, we shall prove a lemma to the effect that for each world in any finite distinguishable model there is a wff which is true in that world but false in all the others.

LEMMA 8.11

Suppose that $\langle W, R, V \rangle$ is a finite distinguishable model. Then for each $w \in W$ there is some wff β_w such that $V(\beta_w, w) = 1$ but $V(\beta_w, w') = 0$ for every $w' \in W$ such that $w' \neq w$.

PROOF

Since W is finite, it consists of a set of worlds $\{w_1, \ldots, w_n\}$, for some $n \geqslant 1$. Since $\langle W, R, V \rangle$ is distinguishable, for each distinct w and $w' \in W$ there is some wff which is true in w but false in w'. Now consider any $w_i \in W$. For each w_j other than w_i, let γ_j be a wff which is true in w_i but false in w_j. Let β_{w_i} be the conjunction of all these γ_js. That is, let β_{w_i} be

$$\gamma_1 \cdot \ldots \cdot \gamma_{i-1} \cdot \gamma_{i+1} \cdot \ldots \cdot \gamma_n$$

Then each conjunct in β_{w_i}, and therefore β_{w_i} itself, is true in w_i; but for each w_j other than w_i, some conjunct in β_{w_i}, and therefore β_{w_i} itself, is false at w_j.

This proves the lemma.

THEOREM 8.12

Suppose that $\langle W, R, V \rangle$ is a finite distinguishable model for a normal modal system S. Then $\langle W, R \rangle$ is a frame for S.

PROOF

To prove the theorem we assume that $\langle W, R \rangle$ is not a frame for S and that $\langle W, R, V \rangle$ is any finite distinguishable model based on $\langle W, R \rangle$; and we show that in that case $\langle W, R, V \rangle$ is not a model for S.

Since $\langle W, R \rangle$ is not a frame for S, there is some theorem α of S which is invalid on $\langle W, R \rangle$. This means that there is some model $\langle W, R, V' \rangle$, based on $\langle W, R \rangle$, such that $V'(\alpha, w^*) = 0$ for some $w^* \in W$. We shall show how to define a wff α' which is a substitution-instance of α, and therefore also a theorem of S, but which is invalid in $\langle W, R, V \rangle$. This will show that $\langle W, R, V \rangle$ is not a model for S.

By hypothesis, $\langle W, R, V \rangle$ is a finite distinguishable model. Therefore, by Lemma 8.11, there is, for each $w \in W$, a wff β_w which in $\langle W, R, V \rangle$ is true in w and nowhere else: for each variable p, let β_p be the disjunction of all the β_ws for which $V'(p, w) = 1$; that is, β_p is

$$\beta_{w_1} \vee \ldots \vee \beta_{w_m}$$

where $w_1, \ldots, w_m$ are all the worlds in which p is true in $\langle W, R, V' \rangle$, and each β_{w_i} $(1 \leqslant i \leqslant m)$ is true in w_i, but nowhere else, in $\langle W, R, V \rangle$. (If $V'(p, w) = 0$ for every $w \in W$, we let β_p be the wff $p . \sim p$.) It is not hard to see that this disjunction will be true in $\langle W, R, V \rangle$ in precisely the worlds in which p is true in $\langle W, R, V' \rangle$. In other words, for all $w \in W$, $V'(p, w) = V(\beta_p, w)$.

Now let δ be any sub-formula of α, and let δ' be the result of uniformly replacing each variable p in δ by the corresponding β_p. It is then a straightforward matter to prove by induction on the construction of a wff, that for every δ and every $w \in W$, $V'(\delta, w) = V(\delta', w)$. In particular, since α is a sub-formula of itself, we have $V'(\alpha, w^*) = V(\alpha', w^*)$. But by hypothesis, $V'(\alpha, w^*) = 0$. Therefore $V(\alpha', w^*) = 0$, and so α', which is clearly a substitution-instance of α, is invalid in $\langle W, R, V \rangle$. As we noted above, this is sufficient to prove the theorem.

COROLLARY 8.13
If a normal modal system has the finite model property, then it has the finite frame property.

COROLLARY 8.14
If a normal modal system has the finite model property, it is complete (i.e. is characterized by some class of frames).

Decidability
A system S (not necessarily a modal system) is said to be *decidable* iff there is an effective procedure whereby, for any given wff α, it can be determined in a finite number of steps whether or not α is a theorem of S. Some systems of logic are known to be decidable, others are known not to be decidable, and of yet others it is not known whether they are decidable or not. This is so for modal as well as for non-modal systems. There is no effective procedure for determining, for an arbitrary system of logic, even for an arbitrary normal modal system, whether or not it is decidable.

We mentioned on p. 136, however, a certain connection

between possession of the finite model property and decidability. We shall now prove that this connection holds.[10]

THEOREM 8.15

If S is a finitely axiomatizable normal modal system which has the finite model property, then S is decidable.

PROOF

Let S be a system of the kind described. Since S is finitely axiomatizable (see p. 6), there is a finite collection A of wff such that the theorems of S are precisely those wff which can be derived from the formulae in A, together with PC-tautologies and **K**, by the rules US, MP and N. This means that any frame $\mathscr{F}$ is a frame for S iff every wff in A is valid on $\mathscr{F}$. Moreover, if $\mathscr{F}$ is finite, there will be a finite (and obviously effective) procedure for checking whether or not all the (finitely many) wff in A are valid on $\mathscr{F}$, and thus whether or not $\mathscr{F}$ is a frame for S. Now it is not difficult to see that, if we disregard isomorphic duplicates, there is an effective procedure for generating all finite frames in some definite order, and therefore for generating all the finite frames for S in some definite order (since each finite frame can be effectively checked for whether or not it is a frame for S). Since S has the finite model property, and therefore the finite frame property, if α is not a theorem of S then it is invalid on some finite frame for S; and therefore, in our effectively generated sequence of finite frames for S there will (eventually!) appear one on which α is invalid.

If α *is* a theorem of S, then of course a frame on which it is invalid will never appear in the sequence we have described. There is, however, also an effective procedure for generating all the proofs of theorems of S in some definite order. (A proof of a theorem α of S is a finite sequence of wff in which each wff is either a PC-tautology, or **K**, or a member of A, or a wff derived from some earlier wff in the sequence by US, MP or N, and in which α is the last member. Clearly α is a theorem of S iff there is such a proof of α.) Hence if α is a theorem of S, a proof of α will (again, eventually!) appear in this generated sequence of proofs.

Since any wff α either is or is not a theorem of S, therefore, either a frame on which α is invalid will appear in a finite number of steps in the first sequence, or a proof of α will appear in a finite number of steps in the second sequence (but not, of course, both).

In the former case, α is not a theorem of S; in the latter case it is. This gives an effective procedure for determining any wff whether or not it is a theorem of S, and so proves the theorem.

(We are not, of course, suggesting that the procedure we have described would be of much use in actual practice for discovering whether some particular formula is a theorem of S or not. For some of the best-known systems more practical procedures are described in chapters 5 and 6 of *IML*, and the methods explained there can easily be adapted for many other systems as well.)

It is important to notice what Theorem 8.15 does not say as well as what it does.

First, it is only for finitely axiomatizable systems that possession of the finite model property guarantees decidability. There are, in fact, systems which have the finite model property but are undecidable, though of course they are not finitely axiomatizable.[11]

Secondly, even if we confine our attention to finitely axiomatizable systems, possession of the finite model property, although a sufficient condition of decidability, is not a necessary one. There are, in fact, finitely axiomatizable systems which are decidable but which lack the finite model property.[12]

Thirdly, Theorem 8.15 does not say that every decidable system with the finite model property is finitely axiomatizable. There are in fact systems of this kind which are not.[13]

Systems without the finite model property

It follows immediately from Corollary 8.14 on p. 152 that any incomplete normal modal system, such as VB, lacks the finite model property. There are, however, some complete systems which also lack it, and it will be the main purpose of this section to prove this.

The first published proof that a system lacks the finite model property was given by Makinson[14] for a system which we shall call 'Mk'. This system can be axiomatized as T +

Mk $(Lp . \sim LLp) \supset M(LLp . \sim LLLp)$

or alternatively, by obvious transformations of **Mk**, as T +

Mk' $L(LLp \supset LLLp) \supset (Lp \supset LLp)$

Makinson does not prove that Mk is complete, and we have ourselves been unable to find either a proof that it is complete or a proof that it is not. But his proof that it lacks the finite model property makes no assumptions about its completeness or incompleteness; and later on in this section we shall discuss some extensions of Mk which are demonstrably complete and whose lack of the finite model property follows easily from Mk's lack of it.

It is easy to see that Mk is contained in S4, for the consequent of Mk′ is simply the special S4 axiom, **4**, and therefore Mk′ is a theorem of S4. Every transitive and reflexive frame, therefore, is a frame for Mk, though, as we shall see, there are non-transitive frames for the system as well.

We shall show that Mk lacks the finite model property by proving two things:

(1) that every non-transitive frame for Mk is infinite; and
(2) that $Lp \supset LLp$ is not a theorem of Mk.

Before we proceed to prove these, let us see how together they will give us the result we want. The reason is this: by (2), $Lp \supset LLp$ is not a theorem of Mk. Therefore if Mk *did* have the finite model property, $Lp \supset LLp$ would have to fail in some model based on a finite frame for Mk. But by (1), all such frames are transitive, and we showed long ago that $Lp \supset LLp$ cannot fail on any transitive frame. So Mk cannot have the finite model property.

Our task is therefore to prove (1) and (2).

As a step towards proving (1) we shall show that, for any $n (\geq 1)$,

$$\mathbf{Mk}_n \quad (Lp . \sim LLp) \supset M^n(L^{n+1}p . \sim L^{n+2}p)$$

is a theorem of Mk. The proof is this: clearly $\mathbf{Mk}_1$ is a theorem, since it is $\mathbf{Mk}$ itself. It will therefore be sufficient to prove that if any $\mathbf{Mk}_i$ is a theorem, so is $\mathbf{Mk}_{i+1}$. We do this as follows:

Hypothesis:	(1) $(Lp . \sim LLp) \supset M^i(L^{i+1}p . \sim L^{i+2}p)$ $[\mathbf{Mk}_i]$
(1) × DR3:	(2) $M(Lp . \sim LLp) \supset M^{i+1}(L^{i+1}p . \sim L^{i+2}p)$
(2) $[Lp/p]$:	(3) $M(LLp . \sim LLLp) \supset M^{i+1}(L^{i+2}p . \sim L^{i+3}p)$
$\mathbf{Mk}$, (3) × Syll:	(4) $(Lp . \sim LLp) \supset M^{i+1}(L^{i+2}p . \sim L^{i+3}p)$
	$[\mathbf{Mk}_{i+1}]$

Now suppose that $\langle W, R \rangle$ is a non-transitive frame for Mk. (It will, of course, be reflexive, since Mk contains T.) This means that there are worlds w_1, w_2 and w_3 in W such that $w_1 R w_2$ and $w_2 R w_3$ but not $w_1 R w_3$, and also that every theorem of Mk is true in every world in every model based on $\langle W, R \rangle$. Consider now such a model in which p is true in every world w_1 can see but false in w_3. Clearly $Lp. \sim LLp$ (the antecedent of each $\mathbf{Mk}_n$) will then be true in w_1. Hence the consequent of each $\mathbf{Mk}_n$ must also be true in w_1. But for this to be so, there must, for every n, be some $w_4 \in W$ in which $L^{n+1}p. \sim L^{n+2}p$ is true; and since R is reflexive, this can be so only if W contains a string of n + 3 distinct worlds beginning with w_4, with each related to the next and p true in all except the last. Since n can be arbitrarily large, W must be infinite. Thus we have established (1).

To prove (2) – that $Lp \supset LLp$ is not a theorem of $\mathbf{Mk}$ – it is sufficient to produce a reflexive frame on which $\mathbf{Mk}$ is valid but $Lp \supset LLp$ is not. The frame that Makinson uses for this purpose is one which has come to be known as the *recession frame*.[15] In this frame W is the set of all the natural numbers, including 0, and R is defined by the condition that, for any w and $w' \in W$, wRw' iff $w' \geqslant w - 1$ (taking $0 - 1$ as 0 itself). What this means is that every number is related to its immediate predecessor, to itself, and to every number greater than it. Thus in any model based on the recession frame, $L\alpha$ will be true at any $w \in W$ iff α is true at $w - 1$ and at all subsequent numbers, $LL\alpha$ will be true at w iff α is true at $w - 2$ and at all subsequent numbers, and so on. Clearly the recession frame is reflexive. To show that $\mathbf{Mk}$ is valid on it, consider any model based on it in which the antecedent of $\mathbf{Mk} - Lp. \sim LLp -$ is true at some $w \in W$. Then p must be true at $w - 1$ and at all subsequent numbers, but false at $w - 2$. But in that case there will be some $w' \in W$, namely $w + 1$, to which w is related and at which LLp is true but $LLLp$ is false. Hence $LLp. \sim LLLp$ is true at $w + 1$, and so $M(LLp. \sim LLLp) -$ the consequent of $\mathbf{Mk}$ – is true at w. Thus $\mathbf{Mk}$ cannot be falsified in any model based on the recession frame, and therefore this is a frame for Mk.

The recession frame, however, is not transitive, since for any $w \geqslant 2$ we have $wRw - 1$ and $w - 1Rw - 2$ but not $wRw - 2$.

By Theorem 5.3, therefore, $Lp \supset LLp$ is not valid on it.

This establishes (2), and thus completes the proof that Mk does not have the finite model property.

The proof we have just given leads easily to the following more general result:

THEOREM 8.16

Suppose that S is a normal modal system which contains Mk, and that the recession frame is a frame for S. Then S lacks the finite model property.

PROOF

It is sufficient to show that (1) and (2) hold of S. The proof that (1) holds is this: since S contains Mk, every frame for S is also a frame for Mk. But as we have shown, every non-transitive frame for Mk is infinite. Therefore every non-transitive frame for S is also infinite. The proof that (2) holds is simply that the recession frame is a frame for S but that $Lp \supset LLp$ fails on it, as we have just shown.

As we remarked on p. 155, we do not know whether or not the system Mk is complete, and so we cannot present it as a clear example of a complete system which lacks the finite model property. There are, however, a number of systems which can easily be shown by Theorem 8.16 to lack the finite model property and are demonstrably complete, and we shall discuss three of these. We shall call them Mk^1, Mk^2 and Mk^3, and they can be axiomatized, respectively, as T +

Mk^1 $L(LLp \supset LLLq) \supset (Lp \supset LL(p \lor q))$
Mk^2 $L(LLp \supset LLLq) \supset (Lp \supset LLq)$
Mk^3 $L(LLp \supset Lq) \supset (Lp \supset q)$

It is easy to see that Mk^3 contains Mk^2, since by substituting LLq for q in **Mk^3** we obtain **Mk^2**. Moreover, since $LLq \supset LL(p \lor q)$ is a theorem even of K, **Mk^1** is easily derivable from **Mk^2**, and so Mk^2 contains Mk^1. Again, by substituting p for q in **Mk^1** and simplifying $p \lor p$ to p, we obtain **Mk$'$**; so Mk^1 contains Mk, and therefore so too do Mk^2 and Mk^3.

To show that the recession frame is a frame for each of these systems it is sufficient to show that it is a frame for the strongest of them, Mk^3. To do this, we first note that Mk^3 can be axiomatized as $T +$

Mk$^{3'}$ $(Lp.q) \supset M(LLp.Mq)$

since each of **Mk**^{3} and **Mk**$^{3'}$ can be obtained from the other by substituting $\sim q$ for q and making straightforward equivalence transformations. It will then be enough to show that **Mk**$^{3'}$ is valid on the recession frame. Suppose, then, that in some model based on the recession frame, $Lp.q$ is true at some $w \in W$. Then p is true at $w - 1$ and at every subsequent number, and therefore LLp is true at $w + 1$. Moreover, q is true at w, and therefore, since $w + 1Rw$, Mq is true at $w + 1$. Thus $LLp.Mq$ is true at $w + 1$; and so, since $wRw + 1$, $M(LLp.Mq)$ is true at w. This is enough to show that **Mk**$^{3'}$ is valid on the recession frame, and therefore that this frame is a frame for Mk^1, Mk^2 and Mk^3.

By Theorem 8.16, therefore, these three systems all lack the finite model property. We have not, however, proved that they are complete. We shall now do this for Mk^3.

The completeness of Mk^3 does in fact follow from the fact that **Mk**$^{3'}$ is an instance of the schema **Sahl** given on p. 46, and therefore corresponds to a first-order condition on a relation. Since **T** obviously also corresponds to such a condition, Mk^3 is not only complete but first-order definable. We have not formulated the general condition which corresponds to **Sahl**, far less proved Sahlqvist's theorem; but in fact the condition which corresponds to **Mk**$^{3'}$ is

(C3) $(\forall w_1)(\exists w_2)(w_1 R w_2 . w_2 R w_1 . (\forall w_3)(w_2 R^2 w_3 \supset w_1 R w_3))$

What C3 means can be expressed thus: every world can see some world which (a) can see it in return, and (b) is such that whatever it can see in two steps, the original world can see in one. It is a simple matter to check that the recession frame satisfies this condition.

We shall, however, especially in view of the fact that we have not proved Sahlqvist's theorem, give a characterization proof for Mk^3.

THEOREM 8.17
Mk^3 is characterized by the class of all reflexive frames which satisfy condition C3.

PROOF

For soundness it is sufficient (since Mk^3 contains T, which corresponds to reflexiveness) to show that $\mathbf{Mk}^3$ is valid in every model which satisfies C3. Let $\langle W, R, V \rangle$ be any such model, and let w_1 be any world in W in which $L(LLp \supset Lq)$ and Lp are both true. It will then be sufficient to show that q is also true in w_1. Now by C3, there is some $w_2 \in W$ such that (i) $w_1 R w_2$, (ii) $w_2 R w_1$, and (iii) w_1 is related to every w_3 to which w_2 is related in two steps. By (i), since $L(LLp \supset Lq)$ is true in w_1, $LLp \supset Lq$ is true in w_2. By (iii), since Lp is true in w_1, p is true in every w_3 to which w_2 is related in two steps. Therefore LLp is true in w_2. We thus have both $LLp \supset Lq$ and LLp true in w_2; therefore Lq is true in w_2. So finally, by (ii), q is true in w_1, as required.

Completeness will be proved if we can show that in the canonical model for Mk^3, R satisfies C3. For this it is sufficient to show that, for any $w_1 \in W$ in that canonical model, the following set of wff is Mk^3-consistent:

$$(\Lambda) \quad L^-(w_1) \cup \{ \sim L\beta : \sim \beta \in w_1 \} \cup \{ LL\gamma : L\gamma \in w_1 \}$$

The reason is this: suppose that Λ is consistent. Then there will be some $w_2 \in W$ which includes it. That being so, (1) since $L^-(w_1) \subseteq w_2$, we have $w_1 R w_2$. (2) Since $\{ \sim L\beta : \sim \beta \in w_1 \} \subseteq w_2$, whenever a wff β is *not* in w_1, $L\beta$ is not in w_2. Therefore whenever $L\beta$ *is* in w_2, β is in w_1, and so we have $w_2 R w_1$. (3) Since $\{ LL\gamma : L\gamma \in w_1 \} \subseteq w_2$, we have, for every $L\gamma \in w_1$, $LL\gamma \in w_2$. Therefore, for every w_3 such that $w_2 R^2 w_3$, we have $\gamma \in w_3$. Thus $L^-(w_1) \subseteq w_3$, and so $w_1 R w_3$, for each such w_3. This means that if Λ is consistent for every $w_1 \in W$, then the canonical model satisfies C3.

Suppose, then, that for some $w_1 \in W$, Λ is not consistent. This means that for some $L\alpha, \sim \beta_1, \ldots, \sim \beta_n$, and $L\gamma$ in w_1,

$$\vdash \sim (\alpha . \sim L\beta_1 . \ldots . \sim L\beta_n . LL\gamma)$$

Then by PC,

$$\vdash \alpha \supset (LL\gamma \supset (L\beta_1 \vee \ldots \vee L\beta_n))$$

Hence by $K[(L\beta_1 \vee \ldots \vee L\beta_n) \supset L(\beta_1 \vee \ldots \vee \beta_n)]$ and PC,

$$\vdash \alpha \supset (LL\gamma \supset L(\beta_1 \vee \ldots \vee \beta_n))$$

Hence by DR1,

$$\vdash L\alpha \supset L(LL\gamma \supset L(\beta_1 \vee \ldots \vee \beta_n))$$

But $L\alpha \in w_1$; therefore

$$L(LL\gamma \supset L(\beta_1 \vee \ldots \vee \beta_n)) \in w_1$$

Hence by **Mk**[3] (with γ for p and $\beta_1 \vee \ldots \vee \beta_n$ for q),

$$L\gamma \supset (\beta_1 \vee \ldots \vee \beta_n) \in w_1$$

But $L\gamma \in w_1$. Therefore $\beta_1 \vee \ldots \vee \beta_n \in w_1$, which contradicts the hypothesis that each of $\sim \beta_1, \ldots, \sim \beta_n$ is in w_1. So Λ is consistent, and the completeness of Mk^3 relative to the stated condition is thereby established.

This completes the proof of Theorem 8.17.

The systems Mk^2 and Mk^1 can be shown to be characterized by the classes of reflexive frames that satisfy the following somewhat forbidding conditions respectively:

(C2) $(\forall w_1)(\forall w_2)(w_1 R^2 w_2 \supset (\exists w_3)(w_1 Rw_3 .(\forall w_4)$
$(w_3 R^2 w_4 \supset w_1 Rw_4).w_3 R^3 w_2))$

(C1) $(\forall w_1)(\forall w_2)(w_1 R^2 w_2 \supset (w_1 Rw_2 \vee (\exists w_3)(w_1 Rw_3 .$
$(\forall w_4)(w_3 R^2 w_4 \supset w_1 Rw_4).w_3 R^3 w_2)))$[16]

We shall not give the characterization proofs for these systems in detail here, but the following hints about the completeness proofs may help readers who wish to work them out for themselves. The key step for Mk^2 is to assume that $w_1 R^2 w_2$, and that therefore whenever $LL\alpha \in w_1, \alpha \in w_2$; and then to use **MK**[2] to prove the consistency of

(Λ') $L^-(w_1) \cup \{LL\beta : L\beta \in w_1\} \cup \{MMM\gamma : \gamma \in w_2\}$

For Mk^1 we assume that $w_1 R^2 w_2$ but not $w_1 Rw_2$, and thus that whenever $LL\alpha \in w_1, \alpha \in w_2$, but that for some $L\delta \in w_1, \sim \delta \in w_2$; and we then use **MK**[1] to prove the consistency of the same set Λ'. It is not difficult to show from the semantic conditions we have mentioned that Mk^3 is stronger than Mk^2 and that Mk^2 is stronger than Mk^1. That Mk^1 is stronger than Mk can be shown in this way: any reflexive frame which satisfies a condition exactly like C1 except that 'R^3' (near the end) is replaced by 'R^4' is a frame for Mk; but the formula **Mk**[1] can be falsified on a frame of this kind. As we have said, we do not know whether Mk is or is not a complete system. Our tentative conjecture is that it is complete but not first-order definable.

The question arises of whether any or all of the systems $Mk-Mk^3$ are decidable. If any of Mk^1-Mk^3 are, then they provide simple examples of systems which are complete, decidable and finitely axiomatizable but which lack the finite model property. We do not know, however, whether they are decidable or not. It may perhaps be wondered whether there are any systems of this kind. But the answer is that there are: for Gabbay[17] has produced a finite axiomatization of the system which is characterized by a frame which is a non-linear version of the recession frame, and has shown that it is decidable; and this system lacks the finite model property.

There are even systems which are finitely axiomatizable and decidable but which are incomplete, and of course these all lack the finite model property. An example is the system characterized by the general frame which we used to study the system VB on pp. 59–62.[18]

Exercises – 8

8.1 Prove that the system MV has the finite model property. (Hint: given a falsifying model for a wff α, form a filtration of this model through the set Φ which consists of all the sub-formulae of $\alpha . L(p . \sim p)$.)

8.2 A *modality* is an unbroken sequence, possibly empty, of monadic operators ($\sim$, L, M). In S4 there are only finitely many non-equivalent modalities (see *IML*, p. 48).

For any wff α, let Φ_α^+ be the set of all wff $A\beta$ where β is any sub-formula of α and A is any modality. Let $\langle W, R, V \rangle$ be a model for S4, and let $\langle W^*, R^*, V^* \rangle$ be a filtration of $\langle W, R, V \rangle$ through Φ_α^+ in which wR^*w' iff, for any $L\beta \in \Phi_\alpha^+$, if $V(L\beta, w) = 1$, then $V(\beta, w') = 1$. Show that R^* is reflexive and transitive, and explain why this shows that S4 has the finite model property.

8.3 Prove that S4.2 has the finite model property. (Hint: use the fact that a generated S4.2 frame is one in which, for every w_1 and w_2, there is some w_3 such that $w_1 R w_3$ and $w_2 R w_3$.)

8.4 (a) Prove that S4.3 is characterized by the class of all finite weakly linear frames.

(b) Let $\mathscr{F}$ be the following frame:

(i) W is the set of all pairs $\langle n, m \rangle$ of natural numbers;

(ii) $\langle n, m \rangle R \langle j, k \rangle$ iff $n \leqslant j$.

Prove that $\mathscr{F}$ characterizes S4.3.

(c) Let $\mathscr{F}$ be the frame just described in (b), except that it is based on the integers instead of the natural numbers. (This means that there is no least number.) Prove that $\mathscr{F}$ characterizes S4.3.

Notes

1 The method is found in Lemmon and Scott (1977). The term 'filtration' itself, however, appears to be due to Segerberg, and so does the proof of the fundamental theorem (our 8.1); see his (1968a).

2 As in the matter of distinguishable models, many authors use the equivalence classes themselves as the members of W*. See note 3, p. 87.

3 Segerberg (1971), p. 67. Segerberg's definition of these terms is, however, slightly different from ours because the worlds in his filtrations are equivalence classes of worlds in the original model.

4 See especially Segerberg (1971), Gabbay (1976) and Chellas (1980). A method of proving that a system has the finite model property without using filtrations may be found in Fine (1975b). Fine's method uses normal forms, and may be applied to all the systems discussed in this section. He is also able to use his method to prove that the system KM (see p. 47 above) has the finite model property, and in this way proves that it is complete (see Corollary 8.14, p. 152). Fine's method can be modified to yield a completeness proof for KM which has affinities with the canonical model type of completeness proof (see Cresswell (1983)).

5 A completeness proof for KW which is in some respects similar to ours is given in Segerberg (1971), pp. 86–8. The system K1.1 referred to in note 6, p. 111, is allied to KW; it is characterized by the class of all finite partial orderings, i.e. finite frames in which R is reflexive, transitive and antisymmetrical (see Segerberg, op. cit., p. 103). Segerberg's proofs are reproduced in chapters 7 and 13 of Boolos (1979). Other filtration proofs for these systems will be found in Gabbay (1976), on pp. 124–7 for KW and on p. 132 for K1.1. Boolos, op. cit., ch. 8, also gives a decision procedure for KW which is similar to the method of semantic diagrams found in Part I of *IML*, and from this procedure he extracts an alternative completeness proof.

All of these proofs can be adapted to deal with systems characterized by frames which are in addition required to be linear. The system characterized by finite strict linear orderings is K4.3W, which we discussed in some detail in chapter 6 (pp. 104–7). The one characterized by finite linear orderings is called S4.3 Grz by Segerberg, op. cit., p. 103, and K3.1 by Sobociński (see *IML*, p. 266). See also Gabbay, op. cit.

6 Segerberg (1971), p. 76.

7 The system characterized by this class is in fact K1.1. See again Segerberg (1971), p. 103; but note that Segerberg's definition of a tree requires that a tree be transitive. In the same work (pp. 94f.) Segerberg refers to the cautionary moral that the present section is designed to emphasize.

8 An even stronger result is known about S4.3. It was proved long ago, in Bull (1966), that not only S4.3 itself, but every normal extension of it, has the finite model property. Bull's proof was algebraic, but the same result has more recently been proved semantically in Fine (1971), Segerberg (1973) and Gabbay (1976). Fine, op. cit., has also proved that every normal extension of S4.3 is finitely axiomatizable; as a result, by Theorem 8.15, p. 153, every such system is decidable. Another result which has been proved about S4.3 (in Segerberg (1975)) is that in any system which contains all the theorems of S4.3 and has the rules US and MP, we can obtain N as a derived rule. In that sense, N would be a redundant item in an axiomatic basis for such a system.

9 Segerberg (1971), p. 33.

10 This theorem is proved in Segerberg (1971), pp. 34–6. Note, however, that Segerberg uses the term 'axiomatizable' to mean what we mean by 'finitely axiomatizable', and uses 'finitely axiomatizable' in the sense explained in note 5, p. 14 above.

11 Urquhart (1981) has produced an example of such a system. Although it is not finitely axiomatizable, its axioms are effectively specifiable.

12 See p. 16.

13 See the proof of this for the system BSeg in Cresswell (1979).

14 Makinson (1969). An extension of S4 without the finite model property is provided in Fine (1972).

15 This name appears to be due to van Benthem (1978), p. 30.

16 Van Benthem (1980), p. 137, claims that Mk is characterized by the class of reflexive frames which satisfy condition C2; but this is incorrect, since this class of frames in fact characterizes Mk^2, which is stronger than Mk.

17 Gabbay (1976), pp. 258–65.

18 Cresswell (1984).

9 Modal predicate logic

This book is basically one about propositional modal logic, and the present chapter is little more than an appendix to those that have preceded it. Clearly we can augment the standard language of predicate logic in the same way as we augmented the language of PC, by adding a monadic operator, L, with an intended modal interpretation. We can then construct a number of systems of modal predicate logic which correspond in fairly obvious ways to various propositional modal systems.

Notation and formation rules for modal LPC

We shall assume throughout a fixed language for the modal lower predicate calculus (modal LPC), except where we speak explicitly of augmenting it, as we do in note 4, p. 185. This language takes as primitive the following symbols:

(1) For each natural number n (≥ 1), a denumerably infinite set of n-place *predicate letters*. We write these as ϕ, ψ, χ, ...
(2) A denumerably infinite set of *individual variables*, which we write as x, y, z, ...
(3) The six symbols $\sim$, $\vee$, L, $\forall$, (and).

The formation rules are these:

FR1 Any expression consisting of an n-place predicate letter followed by n (not necessarily distinct) individual variables is a wff. (Such a wff is called an *atomic wff*.)

FR2 If α is a wff, so are $\sim \alpha$ and $L\alpha$.

FR3 If α and β are wff, so is $(\alpha \vee \beta)$.

FR4 If α is a wff and x is an individual variable, then $(\forall x)\alpha$ is a wff.

We adopt the definitions of ., $\supset$, $\equiv$ and M used in propositional logic, and add the definition:

[Def $\exists$] $(\exists x)\alpha =_{Df} \sim (\forall x) \sim \alpha$

We assume that the reader is familiar with the notions of the scope of a quantifier, free and bound variables, and bound alphabetic variants. These notions are explained in chapter 8 of *IML*, as well as in standard works on predicate logic.

We shall use the notation $\alpha[y/x]$ in the following way. Where α is any wff and x and y are any individual variables, $\alpha[y/x]$ is a wff formed by first taking a bound alphabetic variant of α which has no quantifier in it which contains y, and then replacing every free occurrence of x by y. It should be clear that in $\alpha[y/x]$, y will be free in all those places where it replaces x.[1]

Modal predicate systems

As we did with the propositional systems, and for the same reasons, we shall confine our attention to normal systems; and among normal predicate systems we shall further restrict ourselves to those which have as a theorem the so-called *Barcan* formula, which was discussed in *IML*, pp. 142–5. Expressed as a schema, this formula is

BF $(\forall x)L\alpha \supset L(\forall x)\alpha$

BF is an example of a schema which cannot be stated in propositional modal logic on its own or in non-modal predicate logic on its own. Rather, it expresses a 'mixed' principle which is concerned with the connection between modality and quantification. A great deal of the recent work on modal predicate logic has been concerned with systems some of whose axioms express other mixed principles of this kind. Nevertheless, we shall ignore this work altogether, though in fairness to readers of chapters 10 and 11 of *IML*, where several such formulae were discussed, we feel obliged to point out that a great deal more is now known about the issues raised there. In this chapter we shall confine ourselves to a single question, namely that of how far, and in what ways, some of the properties of propositional modal systems carry over to their predicate logic counterparts; and among the properties in question we shall concentrate mainly on one, completeness.

Our reason for focusing on systems which contain **BF** is not a wish to study any special complexities to which its inclusion may lead. Quite the reverse, in fact, is the case: for it turns out that modal predicate systems which contain **BF** have a simpler semantics than those which do not (see *IML*, pp. 144–8 and 170–4), and as a result, by concentrating on them we shall be able to present the problems in which we are interested here in the simplest and most direct form.

As a preliminary to setting out the systems we intend to study, we define an *LPC substitution-instance* of a wff α of propositional modal logic as any expression which results from uniformly replacing every propositional variable in α by some wff of modal LPC. Clearly every expression so formed is itself a wff of modal LPC.

Suppose, then, that S is any normal modal propositional system. We now define a unique corresponding predicate system, which we shall call S + BF. We present S + BF axiomatically by means of the following axiom schemata and transformation rules:

S: If $\vdash_S \alpha$ and α' is an LPC substitution-instance of α, then α' is an axiom of S + BF.

$\forall 1$:   If α is any wff and x and y are any individual variables, then $(\forall x)\alpha \supset \alpha[y/x]$ is an axiom of S + BF.

BF: If α is any wff and x is any individual variable, then $(\forall x)L\alpha \supset L(\forall x)\alpha$ is an axiom of S + BF.[2]

The transformation rules of S + BF are the familiar MP and N (p. 5), together with

$\forall 2$: $\vdash \alpha \supset \beta \rightarrow \vdash \alpha \supset (\forall x)\beta$

where α and β are any wff and x is any variable which does not occur free in α.

Note that since every normal propositional modal system

contains PC, PC will automatically be a part of every S + BF, in the sense that every LPC substitution-instance of every PC-tautology will be an axiom of S + BF. Note too that if S is axiomatizable, in the sense explained on p. 6, so is S + BF; and in that case the axiom schema S need only specify that every LPC substitution-instance of every *axiom* of S is an axiom of S + BF.

The standard theorems and rules of LPC still hold in every S + BF. We mention in particular the rule of substitution of proved equivalents (Eq), the rule of universal generalization (UG) – i.e. the rule that if $\vdash \alpha$ then $\vdash (\forall x)\alpha$ – and the following theorem schemata:

T1 $(\exists y)(\alpha[y/x] \supset (\forall x)\alpha)$, provided that y does not occur free in $(\forall x)\alpha$.

T2 $(\exists x)(\alpha . \beta) \equiv (\alpha . (\exists x)\beta)$, provided that x does not occur free in α.

T3 $(\forall x)\alpha \equiv (\forall y)\beta$, where α and β differ only in that α has free x where and only where β has free y.

T3 and Eq together yield the rule of replacement of bound alphabetic variants:

RBV The result of replacing any part of a theorem by a bound alphabetic variant of that part is itself a theorem.

From T1 and T2 we can derive the following theorem schema, which will prove useful later on:

T4 $\alpha \supset (\exists y)(\alpha . (\beta[y/x] \supset (\forall x)\beta))$, provided that y is not free in α or in β.

In addition, all the rules of normal propositional modal systems that were mentioned in chapters 1 and 2 carry over to the corresponding predicate systems. The same applies to Theorem 2.2 (p. 19) and Lemma 2.3 (p. 21).

Models

We can study S + BF systems semantically, as we studied normal propositional systems, by means of models, though these will now have to have a somewhat more complex structure. By a *BF model* we mean a triple $\langle \mathscr{F}, D, V \rangle$, where $\mathscr{F}$ is a frame (in the familiar sense of a non-empty set of worlds and a dyadic relation over it), D is a domain of individuals, and V is a value-assignment to the individual variables and the predicate letters[3] which satisfies the following conditions:

(1) For any individual variable x, $V(x) \in D$.
(2) For any n-place predicate letter ϕ, $V(\phi)$ is a set of $n + 1$-tuples $\langle u_1, \ldots, u_n, w \rangle$, where each of $u_1, \ldots, u_n$ is in D and $w \in W$.

Given a BF model $\langle \mathscr{F}, D, V \rangle$, the truth-values of wff at worlds in W are determined by the following rules:

[$V\phi$]   For any n-place predicate letter ϕ and any $w \in W$, $V(\phi x_1 \ldots x_n, w) = 1$ if $\langle V(x_1), \ldots, V(x_n), w \rangle \in V(\phi)$. Otherwise $V(\phi x_1 \ldots x_n, w) = 0$.

[$V\forall$]   For any wff α, any individual variable x and any $w \in W$, $V((\forall x)\alpha, w) = 1$ if for every V' which is just like V except possibly that $V(x) \neq V'(x)$, $V'(\alpha, w) = 1$. Otherwise $V((\forall x)\alpha, w) = 0$.

[$V \sim$], [$V \vee$] and [VL] are exactly as for propositional modal logic (pp. 7f.).

In later sections we shall have occasion to use the following *Principle of Replacement*:

PR   Let $\langle \mathscr{F}, D, V \rangle$ be any BF model, α any wff, and x and y any individual variables. Let $\langle \mathscr{F}, D, V' \rangle$ be a BF model exactly like $\langle \mathscr{F}, D, V \rangle$ except that $V'(x) = V(y)$. Then for every $w \in W$, $V'(\alpha, w) = V(\alpha[y/x], w)$.

The proof is by induction on the construction of a wff, and is a straightforward extension to modal logic of a standard proof for LPC.

Validity and soundness

Our definition of validity for modal LPC will be exactly analogous to our definition for propositional modal systems. If $\langle \mathscr{F}, D, V \rangle$ is a BF model and $\mathscr{F}$ is the frame $\langle W, R \rangle$, we say that a wff α of modal LPC is *valid in* $\langle \mathscr{F}, D, V \rangle$ iff $V(\alpha, w) = 1$ for every $w \in W$. We say that a model $\langle \mathscr{F}, D, V \rangle$ is *based on* the frame $\mathscr{F}$, and that α is *valid on* $\mathscr{F}$ iff it is valid in every BF model based on $\mathscr{F}$. We say that $\mathscr{F}$ is a *frame for* a system S + BF iff every theorem of S + BF is valid on $\mathscr{F}$, and that a class $\mathscr{C}$ of frames *characterizes* S + BF iff, for every wff α of modal LPC, α is valid on every frame in $\mathscr{C}$ iff it is a theorem of S + BF.

A frame in a BF model, of course, is just the same kind of

thing as a frame in a propositional model; so we can speak of one and the same frame as being a frame for a modal propositional system or a frame for a modal predicate system. Our first two theorems state important connections between propositional and predicate systems.

THEOREM 9.1

Suppose that $\mathscr{F}$ is a frame for a normal propositional modal system S. Then $\mathscr{F}$ is a frame for S + BF.

PROOF

Let $\mathscr{C}$ be the class of all BF models based on $\mathscr{F}$. We prove the theorem by showing that each of the axiom schemata of S + BF, viz. S, $\forall 1$ and BF, is valid in every model in $\mathscr{C}$, and then that the transformation rules MP, N and $\forall 2$ preserve the property of being valid in every such model.

(1) For the axiom schema S, we have to verify that if β is a wff of modal LPC obtained by substituting modal LPC wff $\gamma_1, \ldots, \gamma_n$ for propositional variables $p_1, \ldots, p_n$ in some theorem α of S, then β is valid in every model in $\mathscr{C}$. Suppose that β is not valid in every such model, i.e. that for some $\langle \mathscr{F}, D, V \rangle \in \mathscr{C}$ and some $w \in W$, $V(\beta, w) = 0$. Now let $\langle \mathscr{F}, V' \rangle$ be a model for propositional modal logic in which $\mathscr{F}$ is precisely the same frame as in $\langle \mathscr{F}, D, V \rangle$ and in which, for every $w \in W$ and every $p_i (1 \leqslant i \leqslant n)$, $V'(p_i, w) = V(\gamma_i, w)$. Then a straightforward inductive proof will show that $V'(\alpha, w) = 0$, i.e. that α is invalid in $\langle \mathscr{F}, V' \rangle$. Since by hypothesis $\mathscr{F}$ is a frame for S, this means that α is not a theorem of S. Thus if α *is* a theorem of S, β is valid in every model in $\mathscr{C}$.

(2) For $\forall 1$, suppose that for some $w \in W$ in some BF model, $V((\forall x)\alpha, w) = 1$. Then by [V$\forall$], $V'(\alpha, w) = 1$ for every V' which differs from V only in its assignment to x. Among these V's there must be one which assigns to x the same member of D as V assigns to y. Then for this V', by **PR**, $V'(\alpha, w) = V(\alpha[y/x], w)$. But $V'(\alpha, w) = 1$; therefore $V(\alpha[y/x], w) = 1$. This shows that every instance of $\forall 1$ is valid in every BF model, and hence in every model in $\mathscr{C}$.

(3) For BF, suppose that for some $w \in W$, $V((\forall x)L\alpha, w) = 1$. Let V' be any value-assignment which differs from V only in its assignment to x, and let w' be any world in W such that wRw'.

Then by [V∀], $V'(L\alpha, w) = 1$, and hence by [VL], $V'(\alpha, w') = 1$. Since this holds for every V' differing from V only in assignment to x, we thus have $V((\forall x)\alpha, w') = 1$; and since this holds for every w' such that wRw', we finally have $V(L(\forall x)\alpha, w) = 1$. This shows that every instance of BF is also valid in every BF model, and so in every model in $\mathscr{C}$.

(4) MP and N are validity-preserving in a model for the same reasons as in propositional modal logic.

(5) Finally, for ∀2 we assume that $\alpha \supset \beta$ is valid in every model in $\mathscr{C}$, and show that in that case so is $\alpha \supset (\forall x)\beta$ (where x is not free in α). Take any model $\langle \mathscr{F}, D, V \rangle$ (in $\mathscr{C}$), and any $w \in W$ such that $V(\alpha, w) = 1$. Then consider any model $\langle \mathscr{F}, D, V' \rangle$ which differs from $\langle \mathscr{F}, D, V \rangle$ only in the assignment that V' makes to x. Since x does not occur free in α, α must have the same value at w in $\langle \mathscr{F}, D, V' \rangle$ as it does in $\langle \mathscr{F}, D, V \rangle$; i.e. $V'(\alpha, w) = 1$. But $\langle \mathscr{F}, D, V' \rangle$ is based on $\mathscr{F}$, and hence is a member of $\mathscr{C}$; and by hypothesis, $\alpha \supset \beta$ is valid in every model in $\mathscr{C}$; therefore we have $V'(\beta, w) = 1$ for every such $\langle \mathscr{F}, D, V' \rangle$. So by [V∀], $V((\forall x)\beta, w) = 1$. This means that, for any model in $\mathscr{C}$, whenever we have $V(\alpha, w) = 1$, we also have $V((\forall x)\beta, w) = 1$; so $\alpha \supset (\forall x)\beta$ is valid in every such model.

This completes the proof of Theorem 9.1.

The next theorem is the converse of the previous one.

THEOREM 9.2
If $\mathscr{F}$ is a frame for S + BF, then $\mathscr{F}$ is a frame for S.

PROOF
Suppose that $\mathscr{F}$ is not a frame for S. Then there is some model $\langle \mathscr{F}, V \rangle$, based on $\mathscr{F}$, such that for some wff α which is a theorem of S, and some $w^* \in W$, $V(\alpha, w^*) = 0$. Let $p_1, \ldots, p_n$ be the propositional variables in α; let $\phi_1, \ldots, \phi_n$ be n distinct one-place predicate letters and x some individual variable; and let β be the wff of modal LPC which is obtained from α by uniformly replacing $p_1, \ldots, p_n$ by $\phi_1 x, \ldots, \phi_n x$ respectively. Then clearly β is a substitution-instance of α, and is therefore a theorem of S + BF. To show that $\mathscr{F}$ is not a frame for S + BF it is clearly sufficient to exhibit a BF model $\langle \mathscr{F}, D, V' \rangle$, based on $\mathscr{F}$, in which $V'(\beta, w^*) = 0$. This can be accomplished by letting D be a one-membered set $\{u\}$, so that $V'(x) = u$, and by letting $\langle u, w \rangle$ be

in $V'(\phi_i)$ iff $V(p_i, w) = 1$, for each $w \in W$ and each $i(1 \leqslant i \leqslant n)$. By $[V\phi]$, this will have the effect of making each $\phi_i x$ true in $\langle \mathscr{F}, D, V' \rangle$ at precisely those worlds at which p_i is true in $\langle \mathscr{F}, V \rangle$. Since β contains no quantifiers, it is built up from $\phi_1 x, \ldots, \phi_n x$ by $\sim$, $\vee$ and L in precisely the same way as α is from $p_1, \ldots, p_n$. Hence at any $w \in W$, β will have the same truth-value in $\langle \mathscr{F}, D, V' \rangle$ as α has in $\langle \mathscr{F}, V \rangle$; and in particular, $V'(\beta, w^*) = 0$. Thus $\mathscr{F}$ is not a frame for S + BF.

This proves the theorem.

Theorems 9.1 and 9.2 give us

COROLLARY 9.3
$\mathscr{F}$ is a frame for S iff $\mathscr{F}$ is a frame for S + BF.

It follows immediately from Theorem 9.1 that every theorem of K + BF is valid on every frame. Moreover, the soundness results we proved in chapter 1, together with this theorem, show that each of the following systems is sound with respect to the class of frames listed beside it:

    T + BF: reflexive frames
    K4 + BF: transitive frames
    KB + BF: symmetrical frames
    S4 + BF: reflexive transitive frames
    B + BF: reflexive symmetrical frames
    S5 + BF: equivalence frames

Theorem 9.1, in fact, provides us with a general soundness result to the effect that whenever a normal propositional modal system S is sound with respect to a certain class of frames, so is the corresponding predicate system S + BF.

Theorem 9.2, however, although it is the converse of Theorem 9.1, does not give us a corresponding general completeness result, nor does Corollary 9.3 give us a general characterization result. What Theorems 9.1 and 9.2 together tell us about T + BF, for example, is that the class of all frames for T + BF is precisely the class of all reflexive frames – given, that is, the result that we established in chapter 6, that the frames for T itself are precisely the frames that are reflexive. But as we explained on pp. 92f., that result does not prove that T is complete with respect to the class of all such frames; and for just the same reasons, our present result does not give us a completeness result for T + BF either.

The same applies to the other systems listed above. In each case the frames for the system are precisely the frames described alongside, but this tells us nothing about the completeness of these systems. For our completeness proofs for modal LPC we shall use an adaptation of the method of canonical models, and to that we now turn.

The ∀ property

In the next section we are going to define canonical models for S + BF systems, but certain preliminaries are needed first. In the canonical model for a system S + BF we shall, for reasons which will appear later, take as the worlds in the model, not all the sets of wff that are maximal consistent with respect to S + BF, but only those which have in addition a certain property; and in the present section we shall prove some results which involve that property. In what follows, when we speak of a wff, or a set of wff, simply as 'consistent', we of course mean that it is consistent with respect to some given system; but the system in question can be any S + BF system, since our proofs involve only principles which are common to all such systems.

The property we have referred to we call the ∀ *property*. In order to define it we first introduce the notion of a *deductive consequence* of a set of wff with respect to a given system. This is a quite general notion, not restricted to modal logic, though in the present context we shall be concerned with cases in which the wff are wff of modal LPC and the system is an S + BF system. A wff, α, is said to be a deductive consequence of a set of wff, Λ, with respect to a system S, iff there are wff $\beta_1, \ldots, \beta_n$ in Λ such that

$$\vdash_S (\beta_1 \cdot \ldots \cdot \beta_n) \supset \alpha$$

We write '$\Lambda \vdash_S \alpha$' for 'α is a deductive consequence of Λ with respect to S'. It should be clear that in the special case in which Λ is a maximal S-consistent set of wff, $\Lambda \vdash_S \alpha$ iff $\alpha \in \Lambda$. In what follows, S can be any S + BF system, and we shall therefore usually omit the subscript to $\vdash$.

We now define the ∀ property as follows:

A set Λ of wff of modal LPC has the ∀ *property* iff, for every wff α and every individual variable x, if $\Lambda \vdash \alpha[y/x]$ for every variable y, then $\Lambda \vdash (\forall x)\alpha$.

We now prove a number of results involving the ∀ property.

THEOREM 9.4

Suppose that Λ is a set of wff of modal LPC which has the $\forall$ property, and that α is a wff such that $\Lambda \cup \{\alpha\}$ is consistent. Then there is a maximal consistent set Γ of wff which includes $\Lambda \cup \{\alpha\}$ and also has the $\forall$ property.

PROOF

As in the case of propositional modal logic, we can suppose that all the wff of modal LPC are arranged in some determinate order. In particular, this will mean that all universally quantified wff – i.e. all wff of the form $(\forall x)\delta$, where x is any individual variable and δ is any wff – are given in a determinate order. We also suppose that all the individual variables themselves are given in a determinate order. We now define a sequence of wff, $\gamma_0, \gamma_1, \ldots$ as follows:

(1) γ_0 is α
(2) For each n, γ_{n+1} is $\gamma_n . (\delta[y/x] \supset (\forall x)\delta)$, where $(\forall x)\delta$ is the $n + 1^{\text{th}}$ universally quantified wff in the enumeration of wff and y is the first variable in the enumeration of variables such that $\Lambda \cup \{\gamma_n . (\delta[y/x] \supset (\forall x)\delta)\}$ is consistent.

It is not, of course, immediately obvious that there will in each case be a variable available to act as such a y; and if our sequence is to be well defined we have to prove that there must always be one. We do so in this way: by hypothesis, $\Lambda \cup \{\gamma_0\}$ – i.e. $\Lambda \cup \{\alpha\}$ – is consistent. So all we have to show is that for each n, if $\Lambda \cup \{\gamma_n\}$ is consistent, then there is some variable y which makes

(A) $\Lambda \cup \{\gamma_n . (\delta[y/x] \supset (\forall x)\delta)\}$

consistent.

The proof is this: suppose there is no such y. Suppose, that is, that (A) is inconsistent, for every variable y; in other words that

(i) $\Lambda \vdash \sim (\gamma_n . (\delta[y/x] \supset (\forall x)\delta))$

for every y. Now since both γ_n and δ are single formulae, there must be variables which do not occur in either of them. Let z be one of these, and consider the wff $\delta[z/x] \supset (\forall x)\delta$. It should be clear that, since z does not occur in δ, $(\delta[z/x] \supset (\forall x)\delta)[y/z]$ is the very same wff as $\delta[y/x] \supset (\forall x)\delta$; and hence, since z does not occur in γ_n either, that $\sim (\gamma_n . (\delta[z/x] \supset (\forall x)\delta))[y/z]$ is the very same wff as $\sim (\gamma_n \cdot (\delta[y/x] \supset (\forall x)\delta))$. Thus (i) means that we have

$$\Lambda \vdash \sim (\gamma_n \cdot (\delta[z/x] \supset (\forall x)\delta))[y/z]$$

for every y. But by hypothesis, Λ has the $\forall$ property. Hence we have

$$\Lambda \vdash (\forall z) \sim (\gamma_n \cdot (\delta[z/x] \supset (\forall x)\delta))$$

and therefore

(ii) $\Lambda \vdash \sim (\exists z)(\gamma_n \cdot (\delta[z/x] \supset (\forall x)\delta))$

But by T4 (p. 167) and Transposition,

(iii) $\vdash \sim (\exists z)(\gamma_n \cdot (\delta[z/x] \supset (\forall x)\delta)) \supset \sim \gamma_n$

and therefore, from (ii) and (iii), $\Lambda \vdash \sim \gamma_n$. But this means that $\Lambda \cup \{\gamma_n\}$ is inconsistent, which contradicts our initial hypothesis. Thus there must, after all, be some y which makes (A) consistent, which is what we set out to prove.

The sequence $\gamma_0, \gamma_1, \ldots$ is therefore well-defined, and $\Lambda \cup \{\gamma_m\}$ is consistent for every m. Now let Δ_m be $\Lambda \cup \{\gamma_m\}$, and let Δ be the union of all the Δ_ms. Then Δ itself is consistent, for the following reason: consider any finite subset, B, of Δ. A little reflection will show that there must be some γ_m, say γ_k, such that every wff in B is either a member of Λ or a conjunct in γ_k; and this means that if B is inconsistent, so is $\Lambda \cup \{\gamma_k\}$ – i.e. Δ_k. We have, however, just shown that no Δ_m is inconsistent.

Moreover, we can show that any extension of Δ has the $\forall$ property. For let Θ be any set of wff such that $\Delta \subseteq \Theta$, and suppose that for some wff α, $\Theta \vdash \alpha[y/x]$ for every variable y. Then among the members of Δ, and therefore among the members of Θ, there will be some γ_m which contains $\alpha[y/x] \supset (\forall x)\alpha$ as one of its conjuncts. So, since $\Theta \vdash \alpha[y/x]$, we have $\Theta \vdash (\forall x)\alpha$. Thus Θ has the $\forall$ property.

Finally, let Γ be a maximal consistent extension of Δ. Then Γ has the $\forall$ property; and clearly $\Lambda \subseteq \Gamma$.

This completes the proof of Theorem 9.4.

Our next theorem is a kind of analogue of Theorem 2.2 (p. 19).

THEOREM 9.5

Let α be any consistent wff of modal LPC. Then there is some maximal consistent set Γ with the $\forall$ property such that $\alpha \in \Gamma$.

PROOF

By Theorem 9.4 it is sufficient to show that there is some set Λ with the $\forall$ property such that $\Lambda \cup \{\alpha\}$ is consistent. Now for any $S + BF$ system, if β is a theorem, then so, by UG, is $(\forall x)\beta$. Thus the set **Th** of all the theorems of $S + BF$ has the $\forall$ property. Moreover, if α is consistent, so is **Th** $\cup \{\alpha\}$. So **Th** can serve as the required Λ, and this suffices to prove Theorem 9.5.[4]

THEOREM 9.6

Suppose that Γ is a maximal consistent set of wff of modal LPC with the $\forall$ property. Then $L^-(\Gamma)$ also has the $\forall$ property.

PROOF

Suppose that $L^-(\Gamma) \vdash \alpha[y/x]$ for every variable y. Then for every y there are some wff $\beta_1, \ldots, \beta_n \in L^-(\Gamma)$ such that

$$\vdash (\beta_1 \cdot \ldots \cdot \beta_n) \supset \alpha[y/x]$$

Hence by DR1 and L-distribution,

$$\vdash (L\beta_1 \cdot \ldots \cdot L\beta_n) \supset L\alpha[y/x]$$

But clearly $L\beta_1 \cdot \ldots \cdot L\beta_n \in \Gamma$, and so $\Gamma \vdash L\alpha[y/x]$. Since this holds for every variable y, and Γ has the $\forall$ property, we have

$$\Gamma \vdash (\forall x)L\alpha$$

and so, by **BF**,

$$\Gamma \vdash L(\forall x)\alpha$$

Since Γ is maximal consistent, we then have $L(\forall x)\alpha \in \Gamma$, and therefore $(\forall x)\alpha \in L^-(\Gamma)$. Thus $L^-(\Gamma) \vdash (\forall x)\alpha$, and so $L^-(\Gamma)$ has the $\forall$ property. This proves the theorem.

The next theorem is the analogue of Lemma 2.3 (p. 21).

THEOREM 9.7

Suppose that Γ is a maximal consistent set of wff of modal LPC which has the $\forall$ property and contains a wff $\sim L\alpha$. Then there is a maximal consistent set which includes $L^-(\Gamma) \cup \{\sim \alpha\}$ and also has the $\forall$ property.[5]

PROOF

By Lemma 2.3, $L^-(\Gamma) \cup \{\sim \alpha\}$ is consistent. By Theorem 9.6,

$L^-(\Gamma)$ has the ∀ property. The theorem then follows by Theorem 9.4.

Canonical models for S + BF systems

Where S is any normal propositional modal system and S + BF is the corresponding predicate system as defined on p. 166, we now define the *canonical model for S + BF* as the model $\langle \mathscr{F}, D, V \rangle$ in which

(1) $\mathscr{F} = \langle W, R \rangle$, where
    (1a) W is the set of all maximal S + BF-consistent wff of modal LPC with the ∀ property; and
    (1b) For any w and $w' \in W$, wRw' iff $L^-(w) \subseteq w'$.
(2) D is the set of all individual variables.
(3) V is defined as follows:
    (3a) For any individual variable x, $V(x) = x$.
    (3b) For any n-place predicate letter ϕ, any individual variables $x_1, \ldots, x_n$, and any $w \in W$, $\langle x_1, \ldots, x_n, w \rangle \in V(\phi)$ iff $\phi x_1 \ldots x_n \in w$.

(The truth-value assignment rules $[V\phi]$ etc. stated on p. 168 of course apply to $\langle \mathscr{F}, D, V \rangle$ as to all other S + BF models.)

We now state and prove the fundamental theorem for canonical models for S + BF systems.

THEOREM 9.8
If S is a normal modal system and $\langle \mathscr{F}, D, V \rangle$ is the canonical model for S + BF, then for any wff α of modal LPC and any $w \in W$, $V(\alpha, w) = 1$ iff $\alpha \in w$.

PROOF
The proof is by induction on the construction of a wff of modal LPC.

First, suppose that α is an atomic wff, say $\phi x_1 \ldots x_n$. Then for any $w \in W$, by $[V\phi]$

$$V(\phi x_1 \ldots x_n, w) = 1 \text{ iff } \langle V(x_1), \ldots, V(x_n), w \rangle \in V(\phi).$$

Hence, by clause (3a) in the definition of V,

$$V(\phi x_1 \ldots x_n, w) = 1 \text{ iff } \langle x_1, \ldots, x_n, w \rangle \in V(\phi);$$

and so by clause (3b),

$V(\phi x_1 \ldots x_n, w) = 1$ iff $\phi x_1 \ldots x_n \in w$.

Thus the theorem holds if α is any atomic wff.

Let us say that a wff α' is an *individual substitution-instance* of α iff $\alpha' = \alpha[y/x]$ for some variables x and y. We then take as our induction hypothesis that the theorem holds for a wff α and for all individual substitution-instances of α. Clearly, if α is an atomic wff, so is every individual substitution-instance of α; so the proof we have given shows that the hypothesis holds whenever α is atomic.

The inductions for $\sim$, $\vee$ and L are straightforward adaptations of those used in the proof of Theorem 2.4 on pp. 23–5, except that in the induction for L we use Theorem 9.7 instead of Lemma 2.3.

All that remains is the induction for the universal quantifier, which runs as follows: we assume that the induction hypothesis holds for a wff α, and we show that it then holds for $(\forall x)\alpha$.

(a) Suppose that $(\forall x)\alpha \in w$. Then by $\forall 1$, $\alpha[y/x] \in w$ for every variable y. So, by the induction hypothesis, $V(\alpha[y/x], w) = 1$ for every variable y. Now consider any such $\alpha[y/x]$, and let $\langle \mathscr{F}, D, V' \rangle$ be exactly like $\langle \mathscr{F}, D, V \rangle$ except that $V'(x) = V(y)$. Then by **PR** (p. 168), $V'(\alpha, w) = 1$. Clearly we obtain the same result for any other variable y and the corresponding V'; and D is precisely the set of all variables. So what we have proved is that $V'(\alpha, w) = 1$ for every V' which is like V except in the value it assigns to x. Therefore, by $[V\forall]$, $V((\forall x)\alpha, w) = 1$.

(b) Suppose that $(\forall x)\alpha \notin w$. Then, since w has the $\forall$ property, there must be some y such that $\alpha[y/x] \notin w$. So, by the induction hypothesis, $V(\alpha[y/x], w) = 0$. Let $\langle \mathscr{F}, D, V' \rangle$ be exactly like $\langle \mathscr{F}, D, V \rangle$ except that $V'(x) = V(y)$. Then by **PR**, $V'(\alpha, w) = 0$. Hence for some V' which is like V except in the value it assigns to x, $V'(\alpha, w) \neq 1$. Therefore, by $[V\forall]$, $V((\forall x)\alpha, w) \neq 1$.

The arguments in (a) and (b) easily generalize to all individual substitution-instances of $(\forall x)\alpha$.

This completes the induction for the universal quantifier, and with it the proof of Theorem 9.8.

Since every theorem of S + BF is in every world in the canonical model for S + BF, Theorem 9.8 means that every such theorem is valid in the canonical model. Moreover, Theorem 9.5 and the definition of W show that every S + BF-consistent wff is in some world, and therefore, by Theorem 9.8, true in some world in the canonical model; and this in turn means that every non-theorem of S + BF is false in some world in that model. So, to parallel Corollary 2.5 on p. 25, we have

COROLLARY 9.9
Any wff α is valid in the canonical model for S + BF iff $\vdash_{S+BF} \alpha$.

As we explained in chapter 2, a system is complete with respect to a class $\mathscr{C}$ of models iff every wff that is consistent with respect to that system has a verifying model in $\mathscr{C}$. Since the canonical model for S + BF verifies every S + BF-consistent wff, we therefore have

COROLLARY 9.10
Any S + BF system is complete with respect to a class $\mathscr{C}$ of BF models if the canonical model for S + BF is a member of $\mathscr{C}$.

We can now use canonical models to prove the completeness of various modal predicate systems exactly as we used them in chapter 2 to prove the completeness of modal propositional systems. As an example, take T + BF. By Corollary 9.10, if we wish to prove that T + BF is complete with respect to the class of all reflexive BF models (as T itself is with respect to the class of all reflexive propositional models), all we need to show is that the canonical model for T + BF is reflexive. This is easily accomplished, in the same way as the parallel result for T was on p. 28. For since $Lp \supset p$ is a theorem of T, $L\alpha \supset \alpha$ is a theorem of T + BF for every wff α of modal LPC. So every such $L\alpha \supset \alpha$ is in every world w in the canonical model for T + BF, and hence whenever $L\alpha \in w$, we have $\alpha \in w$. Thus $L^-(w) \subseteq w$; i.e. wRw.[6]

A reflexive model, of course, is simply a model based on a reflexive frame; so what we have shown in that T + BF is complete with respect to the class of all reflexive *frames*. We also showed on p. 171 that it is sound with respect to this class of frames. It is therefore characterized by this class.

Clearly, analogous results can be obtained in the same way for many of the other systems we have mentioned, including all those listed on p. 171.

General questions about completeness in modal LPC

On p. 171 we were able to reach a general soundness result connecting the soundness of a normal propositional modal system S with the soundness of the corresponding predicate system S + BF. In this final section we shall enquire whether, and subject to what qualifications, we can obtain any analogous general results about completeness and characterization. We have, of course, in the preceding section, found a method of proving that certain particular S + BF systems are complete, and that they are characterized by certain specified classes of frames. Here, however, we shall be concerned with the general question: suppose we are given, about an arbitrary normal propositional modal system S, information about whether it is or is not complete in the absolute sense explained on p. 55, and (if it is complete) what classes of frames characterize it; what can we deduce from this about the completeness or incompleteness of S + BF and about what classes of frames characterize it?

One result we can certainly establish in this area is that if S is incomplete (in the absolute sense), then S + BF is incomplete too. As a preliminary to proving this, we shall introduce some new terminology and prove a lemma.

Suppose that α is any wff of modal LPC, and that β is an expression which results from α by deleting all quantifiers and individual variables, and uniformly replacing each distinct predicate letter by a distinct propositional variable. Then clearly β is a wff of modal propositional logic; and we shall call it a *propositional transform* of α iff it is derived from α in this way.

Next, let $p_1, p_2, \ldots$, etc., $\phi_1, \phi_2, \ldots$, etc. and $x_1, x_2, \ldots$, etc. be enumerations of the propositional variables, the one-place predicate letters, and the individual variables respectively. Then we shall say that a wff γ of propositional modal logic and a wff δ of modal LPC are *mates* iff δ is the result of uniformly replacing each p_i in γ by $\phi_i x_i$. Clearly, each wff γ of propositional modal logic will have a unique mate δ, and γ will be a propositional transform of δ.

Our lemma is

LEMMA 9.11

Suppose that $\vdash_{S+BF} \alpha$ and that β is a propositional transform of α. Then $\vdash_S \beta$.

PROOF

Since $\vdash_{S+BF} \alpha$, there is a proof of α in $S + BF$. The lemma is then proved by induction on the proof of α in $S + BF$. For if any wff in the proof of α is an instance of the axiom schema S, then its propositional transforms are theorems of S. If it is an instance of $\forall 1$ or BF, then its propositional transforms are substitution-instances of $p \supset p$, and are therefore also theorems of S. The rules MP and N operate in exactly the same way in S and in $S + BF$. And if a wff γ' is derived from γ by $\forall 2$, the propositional transform of γ' is simply identical with that of γ. This shows that a parallel proof of β can be given in S, and hence that $\vdash_S \beta$, which proves the lemma.

COROLLARY 9.12

If γ and δ are mates, then if $\vdash_{S+BF} \delta$, $\vdash_S \gamma$.

THEOREM 9.13

Suppose that a normal propositional modal system S is incomplete. Then so is $S + BF$.

PROOF

Since S is incomplete, there is some wff γ of propositional modal logic which is valid on every frame for S but is not a theorem of S. Let δ be the wff of modal LPC which is the mate of γ. Since δ is a substitution-instance of γ, it is also valid on every frame for S. Therefore by Corollary 9.3, δ is valid on every frame for $S + BF$. But by Corollary 9.12, δ is not a theorem of $S + BF$. So $S + BF$ is incomplete.

This completes the proof.

We know, then, that if S is not characterized by any class of frames, neither is $S + BF$. So the remaining question is: suppose that S is characterized by some class of frames; what can we deduce from that about the characterization of $S + BF$? To make the position clearer, let us distinguish between two things that we might be asking here:

(a) Is it the case that whenever S is characterized by a certain class $\mathscr{C}$ of frames, then $S + BF$ is also characterized by $\mathscr{C}$?

(b) Is it the case that whenever S is characterized by the class of all the frames for S, then S + BF is also characterized by the class of all the frames for S?

(Note that since every system which is characterized by any class of frames at all is characterized by the class of all the frames for that system, (b) is equivalent to the question whether whenever S is complete in the absolute sense, so is S + BF.)

Questions (a) and (b) have to be distinguished, because even if we could answer (b) in the affirmative, it would not follow that the answer to (a) is also in the affirmative. For it might still be that S were characterized by some sub-class of the frames for S but that S + BF was not characterized by that sub-class.

We proved, of course, in Corollary 9.3, that the frames which are frames for S are precisely the frames which are frames for S + BF. But this does not give us an affirmative answer even to question (b); for it still leaves open the possibility that S might be *characterized by* the class of those frames but S + BF might not. Here it may help to recall the discussion of the systems MV and VB on pp. 57–62. We were able to prove that precisely the same frames were frames for these two systems, yet it turned out that the class of these frames characterized one of them but did not characterize the other.

Corollary 9.3 does, however, easily give us this *conditional* answer to (b):

COROLLARY 9.14
If S + BF is complete, then it is characterized by the class of all frames for S.

The proof is simply that any complete system, i.e. any system characterized by any class of frames, is characterized by the class of all the frames for that system, and that by Corollary 9.3 the frames for S + BF are precisely the frames for S. So if a system S + BF is complete, we know of at least one class of frames which characterizes it.

Our next result gives us another conditional answer to (b):

THEOREM 9.15
Suppose that the frame of the canonical model for S + BF is a frame for S. Then S + BF is characterized by the class of all frames for S.

PROOF

Suppose first that α is a theorem of S + BF. Let $\mathscr{F}$ be any frame for S. By Theorem 9.1, $\mathscr{F}$ is also a frame for S + BF, and therefore α is valid on it. So α is valid on every frame for S. Suppose now that α is not a theorem of S + BF. Then $\sim \alpha$ is S + BF-consistent, and therefore is in some $w \in W$ in the canonical model for S + BF. So by Theorem 9.8, $V(\alpha, w) = 0$. But by hypothesis the frame of the canonical model is a frame for S. Therefore α fails on some frame for S.

This means that, given the hypothesis of the theorem, any wff α of modal LPC is valid on all frames for S iff $\vdash_{\text{S + BF}} \alpha$, which is what the theorem states.

COROLLARY 9.16

If the frame of the canonical model for S + BF is a frame for S, then S + BF is characterized by any class of frames for S which contains the frame of the canonical model for S + BF.

Proving that the frame of the canonical model for S + BF is a frame for S is, of course, precisely what we did in the case of T + BF on p. 178; and as we mentioned there, we can obtain analogous results for many other S + BF systems. But this is still far short of showing that whenever S is complete, S + BF is also complete, since in some cases we might not be able to prove that the frame of the canonical model for S + BF *is* a frame for S.

So far we have been concerned with question (b) on p. 181. If we turn to question (a), however, we can answer it definitely in the negative: it is *not* the case that whenever a normal propositional modal system S is characterized by a certain class of frames, the corresponding predicate system S + BF is characterized by that class. A single counter-example will suffice. The propositional system K, as we know, is characterized by the class of all frames; it also has the finite model property, and is therefore characterized by the class of all finite frames. But although K + BF is also characterized by the class of all frames, it is not characterized by the class of all finite frames. To prove this, it is sufficient to produce a K + BF-consistent wff α which is false at every world in every finite BF model; for then $\sim \alpha$ will not be a theorem of K + BF, but it will be valid on all finite frames. Consider the formula

$$(*) \ (\forall x)(\forall y)(\forall z)((\phi xy . \phi yz) \supset \phi xz) . (\forall x) \sim \phi xx .$$
$$(\forall x)(\exists y)\phi xy . (\forall x)(\forall y)((M\phi xy \supset \phi xy) . (\phi xy \supset L\phi xy))$$
$$. (\forall x)M(\psi x . (\forall y)(\phi xy \supset \sim \psi y))$$

The first three conjuncts in (*) say that ϕ is transitive, irreflexive and serial. For these all to be true at a world w_0 in a BF model, the domain must be infinite, and in w_0 there must be at least one infinite linear sequence A of objects in which each is ϕ-related to all its successors but to none of the others. The fourth conjunct says that if any two objects are ϕ-related in any world accessible from w_0, they are also ϕ-related in w_0 itself and in *every* world accessible from w_0. The final conjunct says that for each object, u_i, there is some world w_i accessible from w_0 in which it has a certain property ψ, but nothing to which u_i is ϕ-related also has ψ. A little reflection will show that this can be so if, but only if, each distinct $u_i \in A$ is ψ in a distinct w_i accessible from w_0. This means that (*) can be true somewhere in an infinite BF model, but must be false everywhere in any finite one. So its negation can be falsified in a BF model, and is thus not a theorem of K + BF, but it is valid in every finite (K + BF) model. This shows that K + BF, unlike K itself, does not possess the finite model property, and so there is a class of frames (the class of all finite frames) which characterizes K but does not characterize K + BF.

Our question (a), then has to be answered in the negative. But we have not given any general answer, affirmative or negative, to question (b). That question, it may be recalled, amounted to the question whether, given that a propositional normal modal system S is complete (in the absolute sense), it always follows that S + BF is also complete. We have seen that in many particular cases this does follow. But the only general results linking the characterization of a propositional system with its predicate counterpart have been Corollary 9.14 and Theorem 9.15. These, however, are only conditional results. For they merely say, respectively, that *if* S + BF is complete, and that *if* the canonical model for S + BF is a frame for S, then S + BF is characterized by all the frames for S itself; and this still does not answer the question of whether we can always infer the completeness of S + BF from the completeness of S. This is surely one of the most important questions in modal predicate logic; yet, as far as we are aware, it is still an open one.

Exercises – 9

9.1 Prove the following in S + BF, where S satisfies the conditions indicated:

   (i) $(\forall x)L(\alpha \supset \beta) \supset L((\exists x)\alpha \supset (\exists x)\beta)$ (where S is any normal system)

   (ii) $(\exists y)LM(\phi y \supset (\forall x)\phi x)$ (where S contains B)

   (iii) $(\exists x) L(L\phi x \vee \psi y) \equiv L(\exists x)(L\phi x \vee \psi y)$ (where S contains S5)

   (iv) $(\exists y)L(\forall x)(L\phi x \supset ML\phi y)$ (where S contains S4.2)

9.2 Prove that if S is a consistent normal propositional modal system, then S + BF is also consistent.

9.3 Given that S contains S4, prove that if Λ is a maximal S + BF-consistent set of wff with the $\forall$ property, then

$$\{L\alpha : L\alpha \in \Lambda\}$$

has the $\forall$ property.

9.4 Use the methods of chapter 7, in conjunction with Theorem 9.7, to prove (a) that K + BF is characterized by the class of all trees, and (b) that S4 + BF is characterized by the class of all reflexive transitive trees.

9.5 (a) Prove that KW + BF is not canonical.

   (b) Is KW + BF complete? (As far as we are aware, this is an open question.)

9.6 Given that S is canonical, does it follow that S + BF is also canonical? (As far as we are aware, this is also an open question.)

Notes
1 This notation (using **a** and **b** instead of x and y) was introduced in *IML* on p. 159, but the explanation of it given there did not guarantee, as our present account does, that for every α, x and y there *is* a wff $\alpha[y/x]$.

2 For some systems, **BF** is derivable from the rest of the basis. This is

certainly so for any S which contains **KB**. (The proof is the one given for S5 on p. 145 of *IML*.)

3 As in chapter 8 of *IML*, we have let V assign values both to the predicate letters and to the individual variables. It is, however, sometimes convenient to distinguish between an *interpretation* of the predicate letters and an *assignment*, within that interpretation, to the individual variables. The rule [V∀] (p. 168) then refers to all assignments within an interpretation which agree on all variables except possibly x. Truth with respect to an assignment of values to the individual variables is sometimes spoken of as *satisfaction* by those values.

4 Theorems 9.4 and 9.5, omitting the word 'modal', are in fact meta-theorems of ordinary LPC. Moreover, a stronger form of Theorem 9.5 can be proved, to the effect that not merely any single consistent wff, but any consistent set, A, of wff, can be extended to a maximal consistent set with the ∀ property. There is obviously no difficulty in proving this if A is finite, since we can then simply treat it as the conjunction of all its members. If, however, A is infinite, we cannot obtain our result as a straightforward application of Theorem 9.4. The standard method of proving the strengthened form of Theorem 9.5 involves adding to the language a denumerable infinity of new variables, none of which occurs in A. This enables us to add successively the required formulae $\delta[y/x] \supset (\forall x)\delta$ in a way which preserves consistency, by choosing y from the stock of new variables in each case. This method is a standard one for LPC and carries over to the modal LPC systems. This strengthened form of Theorem 9.5 has the consequence that, for any S + BF system, if A is any S + BF-consistent set of wff, then there is a world w in the canonical model for S + BF, as defined on p. 176, such that $A \subseteq w$.

5 The proof of this theorem, and its use in completeness proofs for modal predicate logic, is due in its essentials to R.H. Thomason (1970), though Thomason considers only S4. The present method replaces the rather elaborate construction involving E_M-formulae which was given in chapter 9 of *IML*. A somewhat different kind of completeness proof for modal predicate systems will be found in Fine (1978), pp. 131–5. For many of the systems without the Barcan Formula we can use a version of Theorem 8.7 for which (in the manner referred to in note 4, above) we extend the language by introducing infinitely many new variables which do not occur in $L^-(\Gamma)$. Proofs along these lines are given in chapter 10 of *IML* and in Bowen (1979).

6 The subordination technique of chapter 7 can also be extended to apply to modal LPC systems. The completeness proofs in Part II of *IML* were in fact of this character.

Bibliography

Except in the case of *IML*, each item is followed by a list of the numbers of the notes in which it is referred to. (**4.3**) indicates note 3 to chapter 4, etc.

Benthem, J.F.A.K. van (1975) 'A note on modal formulae and relational properties', *Journal of Symbolic Logic*, 40, 55–8 (**3.3**).

(1978) 'Two simple incomplete logics', *Theoria*, 44, 25–37 (**4.3, 4.6, 8.15**).

(1979a) 'Canonical modal logics and ultrafilter extensions', *Journal of Symbolic Logic*, 44, 1–8 (**5.6, 6.6**).

(1979b) 'Syntactic aspects of modal incompleteness theorems', *Theoria*, 45, 63–77 (**4.3, 4.4, 4.5, 6.5**).

(1980) 'Some kinds of modal completeness', *Studia Logica*, 39, 125–41 (**1.5, 5.6, 6.10, 8.16**).

Benthem, J.F.A.K. van and Blok, W.J. (1978) 'Transitivity follows from Dummett's axiom', *Theoria*, 44, 117f. (**6.6**).

Blok, W.J. (1980) 'The lattice of modal logics: an algebraic investigation', *Journal of Symbolic Logic*, 45, 221–36 (**4.3**).

Boolos, G. (1979) *The Unprovability of Consistency*, Cambridge, Cambridge University Press (**6.4, 6.5, 6.6, 8.5**).

(1980) 'On systems of modal logic with provability interpretations', *Theoria*, 46, 7–18 (**4.3**).

Bowen, K.A. (1979) *Model Theory of Modal Logic*, Dordrecht, Reidel (**9.5**).

Bull, R.A. (1966) 'That all normal extensions of S4.3 have the finite model property', *Zeitschrift für mathematische Logik und Grundlagen der Mathematik*, 12, 609–16 (**8.8**).

Chellas, B.F. (1980) *Modal Logic: An Introduction*, Cambridge, Cambridge University Press (**1.9, 1.10, 3.1, 8.4**).

Cresswell, M.J. (1979) 'BSeg has the finite model property', *Bulletin of the Section of Logic, Polish Academy of Sciences*, 8, 154–60 (**8.13**).

    (1982) 'A canonical model for S2', *Logique et Analyse*, 97, 3–7 (**1.8**).

    (1983) 'KM and the finite model property', *Notre Dame Journal of Formal Logic*, 24, 323–7 (**8.4**).

    (1984) 'An incomplete decidable modal logic', *Journal of Symbolic Logic* (forthcoming) (**4.5, 8.18**).

Fine, K. (1971) 'The logics containing S4.3', *Zeitschrift für mathematische Logik und Grundlagen der Mathematik*, 17, 371–6 (**8.8**).

    (1972) 'Logics containing S4 without the finite model property', in Hodges, W. (ed.) *Conference in Mathematical Logic—London '70*, Berlin, Springer-Verlag, 98–102 (**8.14**).

    (1974a) 'Logics containing K4, part I', *Journal of Symbolic Logic*, 39, 31–42 (**6.7**).

    (1974b) 'An incomplete logic containing S4', *Theoria*, 40, 23–9 (**4.3**).

    (1974c) 'An ascending chain of S4 logics', *Theoria*, 40, 110–16 (**4.3**).

    (1975a) 'Some connections between elementary and modal logic', in Kanger, S. (ed.) *Proceedings of the Third Scandinavian Logic Symposium*, Amsterdam, North Holland, 15–39 (**4.2**).

    (1975b) 'Normal frames in modal logic', *Notre Dame Journal of Formal Logic*, 16, 229–37 (**8.4**).

    (1978) 'Model theory for modal logic, part I, the *de re/de dicto* distinction', *Journal of Philosophical Logic*, 7, 125–56 (**9.5**).

Gabbay, D.M. (1976) *Investigations in Modal and Tense Logics with Applications to Problems in Philosophy and Linguistics*, Dordrecht, Reidel (**8.4, 8.5, 8.8, 8.17**).

Goldblatt, R.I. (1975a) 'First-order definability in modal logic', *Journal of Symbolic Logic*, 40, 35–40 (**3.3**).

    (1975b) 'Solution to a completeness problem of Lemmon and Scott', *Notre Dame Journal of Formal Logic*, 16, 405–8 (**3.2**).

    (1976) 'Metamathematics of modal logic', *Reports on Mathematical Logic*, 6, 41–77 (part I); 7, 21–52 (part II) (**3.3, 4.6**).

Goldblatt, R.I. and Thomason, S.K. (1975) 'Axiomatic classes in propositional modal logic', in Crossley, J.N. (ed.) *Algebraic Logic*, Berlin, Springer, 163–73 (**5.6**).

Hughes, G.E. and Cresswell, M.J. (1968) *An Introduction to Modal Logic* (*IML*), London, Methuen (reprinted with corrections, 1972).

    (1975) 'Omnitemporal logic and converging time', *Theoria*, 41, 11–34 (**1.5, 7.2**).

    (1982) 'K1.1 is not canonical', *Bulletin of the Section of Logic, Polish Academy of Sciences*, 11, 109–13 (**6.6**).

Lemmon, E.J. and Scott, D.S. (1977) *The 'Lemmon Notes': An Introduction to Modal Logic*, ed. K. Segerberg, Oxford, Blackwell (**1.2, 1.6, 1.9, 1.10, 2.1, 2.4, 2.5, 3.1, 3.2, 3.3, 4.1, 5.4, 5.5, 6.2, 6.3, 8.1**).

Makinson, D.C. (1969) 'A normal modal calculus between T and S4 without the finite model property', *Journal of Symbolic Logic*, 34, 35–8 (**8.14**).

188 A COMPANION TO MODAL LOGIC

(1970) 'A generalisation of the concept of a relational frame for modal logic', *Theoria*, 36, 331–5 **(4.6)**.

(1971) 'Some embedding theorems in modal logic', *Notre Dame Journal of Formal Logic*, 12, 252–4 **(2.6)**.

Prior, A.N. (1967) *Past, Present and Future*, Oxford, Clarendon Press **(2.7)**.

Routley, F.R. (1970) 'Extensions of Makinson's completeness theorems in modal logic', *Zeitschrift für mathematische Logik und Grundlagen der Mathematik*, 16, 239–56 **(1.8)**.

Sahlqvist, H. (1975) 'Completeness and correspondence in first and second order semantics for modal logic', in Kanger, S. (ed.) *Proceedings of the Third Scandinavian Logic Symposium*, Amsterdam, North Holland, 110–43 **(3.2, 3.4, 7.1)**.

Schumm, G.F. (1972) 'T, S4 and Henkinesque trees', *Journal of Symbolic Logic*, 37, 446 (abstract) **(7.1)**.

Segerberg, K. (1968a) 'Decidability of S4.1', *Theoria*, 34, 7–20 **(5.1, 8.1)**.

(1968b) *Results in Non-classical Logic*, Lund, Berlingska Boktryckeriet **(4.1)**.

(1970) 'Modal logics with linear alternative relations', *Theoria*, 36, 301–22 **(7.4)**.

(1971) *An Essay in Classical Modal Logic* (3 vols), Uppsala, Filosofiska Studier **(1.3, 1.5, 1.7, 1.8, 1.9, 1.10, 2.7, 4.2, 5.1, 5.2, 5.3, 5.7, 5.8, 6.4, 6.6, 6.8, 7.1, 8.3, 8.4, 8.5, 8.6, 8.7, 8.9, 8.10)**.

(1972) 'Post completeness in modal logic', *Journal of Symbolic Logic*, 37, 711–15 **(2.6)**.

(1973) 'Franzen's proof of Bull's theorem', *Ajatus*, 35, 216–21 **(8.8)**.

(1975) 'That every extension of S4.3 is normal', in Kanger, S. (ed.) *Proceedings of the Third Scandinavian Logic Symposium*, Amsterdam, North Holland, 194–6 **(8.8)**.

Thomason, R.H. (1970) 'Some completeness results for modal predicate calculi', in Lambert, K. (ed.) *Philosophical Problems in Logic*, Dordrecht, Reidel, 56–76 **(9.5)**.

Thomason, S.K. (1972a) 'Semantic analysis of tense logics', *Journal of Symbolic Logic*, 37, 150–8 **(4.6, 4.7)**.

(1972b) 'Noncompactness in propositional modal logic', *Journal of Symbolic Logic*, 37, 716–20 **(6.7)**.

(1974) 'An incompleteness theorem in modal logic', *Journal of Symbolic Logic*, 40, 30–4 **(4.3)**.

Urquhart, A. (1981) 'Decidability and the finite model property', *Journal of Philosophical Logic*, 10, 367–70 **(1.4, 8.11)**.

Zeman, J.J. (1973) *Modal Logic: The Lewis Systems*, Oxford, Clarendon Press **(1.10)**.

Glossary

The references in brackets are to the pages on which the terms are first defined or explained. In some cases the definitions in the text are more precise than the ones given here. Italics indicate cross-references within the glossary itself.

Accessibility relation: The relation R in a *model* or *frame* (7).

Allowable set of worlds: See *general frame*.

Amalgamation: *Model* formed from a finite set of models by adding a single extra *world* related to each world in the original models (98).

Antisymmetrical frame (model): *Frame* (*model*) in which R is **antisymmetrical** over W, i.e. is such that for any w and $w' \in W$, if wRw' and $w'Rw$, then $w = w'$ (50).

∀ **property:** Property possessed by a set Λ of wff of modal LPC when, for every α and x, if $\Lambda \vdash \alpha[y/x]$ for every y, then $\Lambda \vdash (\forall x)\alpha$ (172).

Bulldozing: Method of obtaining an *antisymmetrical frame* or *model* from a given *transitive frame* or model (84–6).

$\mathscr{C}$ **model:** Member of a class $\mathscr{C}$ of *models* (16).

$\mathscr{C}$**-valid:** *Valid* in all $\mathscr{C}$ *models* (16).

Canonical model (for propositional system S): *Model* $\langle W, R, V \rangle$ where W is the set of all *maximal S-consistent sets of wff*, wRw' iff $L^-(w) \subseteq w'$, and $V(p, w) = 1$ iff $p \in w$ (22f.). **Canonical model for S + BF system:** see p. 176.

189

Canonical system: *System* S where the *frame* of the *canonical model for* S is a *frame for* S (56).

Characterization: A *system* is characterized by a class $\mathscr{C}$ of *models* or *frames* iff it is both *sound* and *complete* with respect to $\mathscr{C}$ (12, 55).

Closure under sub-formulae: A set Λ of wff is closed under sub-formulae iff, if $\alpha \in \Lambda$ and β is a sub-formula (well-formed part) of α, then $\beta \in \Lambda$ (136).

Cluster: Subset A of W in a *transitive frame* $\langle$ W, R $\rangle$, such that R is *universal* over A but is not universal over any subset of W which properly includes A (82). See also *proper cluster*.

Cohesive frame: *Frame* in which each *world* is related to each other world in some number of backward-or-forward R-steps (78).

Compactness: A *system* S is compact iff every S-*consistent* set of wff is simultaneously *satisfiable* in some *frame for* S (104).

Completeness: (a) A *system* S is complete with respect to a class $\mathscr{C}$ of *models* (*frames*) iff every wff which is *valid* in every model in $\mathscr{C}$ (*valid* on every frame in $\mathscr{C}$) is a theorem of S (12, 54f.). (b) S is absolutely complete iff it is *characterized* by some class of frames (55).

Connected frame (model): *Frame* (*model*) in which R is connected over W, i.e. is such that for any w_1, w_2 and $w_3 \in W$, if $w_1 R w_2$ and $w_1 R w_3$, then $w_2 R w_3$ or $w_3 R w_2$ (30). See also *totally connected* and *weakly connected*.

Consistency: Where S is a *system*, a wff α is S-consistent iff $\dashv_S \sim \alpha$ (17); a finite set of wff $\{\alpha_1, \ldots, \alpha_n\}$ is S-consistent iff $\dashv_S \sim (\alpha_1, \ldots, \alpha_n)$ (17); a set Λ of wff is S-consistent iff every finite subset of Λ is S-consistent (17f.). A system S is consistent iff S is S-consistent (so that S is inconsistent iff every wff is a theorem of S) (4, 18).

Convergent frame (model): *Frame* (*model*) in which R is convergent over W, i.e. is such that for any w_1, w_2 and $w_3 \in W$, if $w_1 R w_2$ and $w_1 R w_3$, then for some $w_4 \in W$, both $w_2 R w_4$ and $w_3 R w_4$ (31).

Dead end: *World* in *frame* not related to any world (9).

Deductive consequence: A wff α is a deductive consequence of a set Λ of wff, with respect to a *system* S (in symbols: $\Lambda \vdash_S \alpha$) iff for some $\beta_1, \ldots, \beta_n \in \Lambda, \vdash_S (\beta_1 \cdot \ldots \cdot \beta_n) \supset \alpha$ (172).

Distinguishable model: *Model* in which for each pair w and w' of distinct worlds there is some wff α such that $V(\alpha, w) \neq V(\alpha, w')$ (75).

Equivalence class of worlds: Class of all the *worlds* in a *model* which are equivalent to a given $w \in W$ by some *equivalence relation* (75f.). A special case is the relation of being *equivalent worlds*.

Equivalence relation (class): A relation R is an equivalence relation over a class A iff R is (i) reflexive, in that for all $x \in A$, xRx, (ii) transitive, in that for all x, y and $z \in A$, if xRy and yRz then xRz, and (iii) symmetrical, in that for all x and $y \in A$, if xRy then yRx. An **equivalence class** with respect to such a relation R is a subclass, B, of A such that for some $x \in A$, $y \in B$ iff yRx (12, 75f.).

Equivalent models (frames): *Models (frames)* which validate precisely the same wff (69).

Equivalent worlds: *Worlds* w and w' in a *model* such that for every wff α, or for every wff α in a given set of wff, $V(\alpha, w) = V(\alpha, w')$ (75, 137).

Failing on a frame: A wff α fails on a *frame* iff it is not *valid* on that frame (54).

Filtration: *Distinguishable model* (in certain important cases finite) obtained from another *model* by omitting all but one *world* from each *equivalence class of worlds*, and satisfying conditions stated on p. 138.

Finite frame property: Property of being *characterized* by a class of *frames* each of which is finite (150).

Finite model property: Property of being *characterized* by a class of *models* each of which is finite (135f.).

Finitely axiomatizable system: *System* all of whose *theorems* can be derived from a finite number of wff by the rules US, MP and N (6).

First-order definable system: *System characterized* by a class of frames in which R satisfies a condition expressible by a formula of first-order predicate calculus with identity (46f.).

Frame. A structure $\langle W, R \rangle$, where W is a non-empty set and R is a dyadic relation defined over it (54).

Frame for a system S: *Frame* on which every *theorem* of S is *valid* (54).

General frame: A structure $\langle W, R, P \rangle$ in which $\langle W, R \rangle$ is a *frame* and P is a collection of 'allowable' sets of *worlds*, specified in such a way that if the property of being true at all and only the worlds in some allowable set belong to all the variables, it also belongs to every wff. An allowable *model* on such a frame is one in which the variables have this property (63).

Generated frame (model): *Frame* (*model*) in which there is some world (a 'generating' world) which is related to each other world in some number of steps (78).

Generated sub-frame: *Sub-frame* $\langle W', R' \rangle$ of some given frame $\langle W, R \rangle$, where W' consists of some world in W together with all worlds accessible from it in any number of R-steps (79).

Irreflexive frame (model): *Frame* (*model*) in which R is *irreflexive* over W, i.e. is such that for every $w \in W$, not wRw (47).

Isomorphic frames (models): *Frames* (*models*) having identical structures (69f.).

Linear frame (model): *Frame* (*model*) which is *reflexive, transitive, totally connected* and *antisymmetrical* over W (83). See also *weakly linear frame* and *strict linear frame*.

Maximal S-consistent set of wff: Set of wff which is both *maximal* and *S-consistent* (18).

Maximal set of wff: Set of wff which contains either α or $\sim \alpha$ for every wff α (18).

Model: (a) For propositional *systems*, a structure $\langle W, R, V \rangle$, where $\langle W, R \rangle$ is a *frame* and V is a *value-assignment* to the variables (7). (b) For S + BF systems, see pp. 167f.

Model for a system S: *Model* in which every theorem of S is *valid* (49).

Normal modal system: See *system*.

Post-complete system: *Consistent system* which cannot be strengthened without becoming inconsistent (35).

Proper cluster: *Cluster* with two or more members (82f.).

Pseudo-epimorphism (p-morphism): Validity-preserving relation between two *frames* or *models*, satisfying the condition stated on pp. 70f.

Reflexive frame (model): *Frame* (*model*) in which R is **reflexive** over W, i.e. is such that for every $w \in W$, wRw (12).

Satisfiability in a frame: A wff α is satisfiable in a *frame* iff it is true at some world in some *model* based on that frame. A set of wff **is simultaneously satisfiable** in a frame iff all its members are true together at some world in some model based on that frame (103).

Serial frame (model): *Frame* (*model*) in which R is **serial** over W, i.e.

is such that for every $w \in W$ there is some $w' \in W$ for which wRw' (29).

Soundness: A *system* S is sound with respect to a class $\mathscr{C}$ of *models* (*frames*) iff every *theorem* of S is *valid* in every model in $\mathscr{C}$ (*valid* on every frame in $\mathscr{C}$) (12, 54).

Strict linear frame (model): *Frame* (*model*) which is *irreflexive*, *transitive* and *weakly connected* (105).

Sub-frame: A *frame* $\langle W', R' \rangle$ is a sub-frame of $\langle W, R \rangle$ iff W' is a subset of W and R' is the restriction of R to W' (79).

Sub-model: A *model* $\langle W', R', V' \rangle$ is a sub-model of $\langle W, R, V \rangle$ iff $\langle W', R' \rangle$ is a *sub-frame* of $\langle W, R \rangle$ and V' = V for all $w \in W'$ (79).

Suitability: Condition to be satisfied by the relation R* in a *filtration*, as defined on p. 138.

Symmetrical frame (model): *Frame* (*model*) in which R is **symmetrical** over W, i.e. is such that for any w and $w' \in W$, if wRw' then $w'Rw$ (12).

System: A **normal modal propositional system** is a class of formulae of modal propositional logic which contains all PC-tautologies and the wff $L(p \supset q) \supset (Lp \supset Lq)$, and satisfies the rules US, MP and N (4f.). **A normal modal predicate system** is defined analogously (165f.). Non-normal modal systems usually differ from normal ones in lacking or restricting N.

Theorem: A wff α is a theorem of a *system* S iff $\alpha \in S$ (4).

Totally connected frame (model): *Frame* (*model*) in which R is **totally connected** over W, i.e. is such that for any w and $w' \in W$, either wRw' or $w'Rw$ (82). Cf. *connected*.

Transitive frame (model): *Frame* (*model*) in which R is **transitive** over W, i.e. is such that for any w_1, w_2 and $w_3 \in W$, if w_1Rw_2 and w_2Rw_3, then w_1Rw_3 (12).

Universal relation: A relation R is universal over a set A iff for every x and $y \in A$, xRy (123).

Validating model for a wff α: *Model* in which α is *valid* (69).

Validity: (a) A wff α is valid in a *model* $\langle W, R, V \rangle$ iff for every $w \in W$, $V(\alpha, w) = 1$ (9). (b) A wff is valid on a *frame* $\langle W, R \rangle$ iff it is valid in every *model* based on $\langle W, R \rangle$ (54). (c) A wff is valid with respect to a class of *models* (*frames*) iff it is valid in every model (on every frame) in the class in question (9, 54). See also $\mathscr{C}$-*valid*.

Validity-preservingness: (a) A transformation rule is validity-preserving iff all the formulae which result from applying it to *valid* formulae are themselves valid (9f.). (b) An operation on a *frame* (*model*) is validity-preserving iff every formula which is valid on the original frame (model) is valid on the frame (model) produced by the operation (87).

Value-assignment: (a) For propositional systems, a specification for each variable p and each *world* w in a *model*, whether $V(p, w) = 1$ or $V(p, w) = 0$ (7f.). (b) For S + BF systems, see p. 167f.

Verifying model for a wff α: *Model* $\langle$ W, R, V $\rangle$ in which for some $w \in W$, $V(\alpha, w) = 1$ (17).

Weakly connected frame (model): *Frame* (*model*) in which R is **weakly connected** over W, i.e. is such that for any w_1, w_2 and $w_3 \in W$, if $w_1 R w_2$ and $w_1 R w_3$ then either $w_2 = w_3$ or $w_2 R w_3$ or $w_3 R w_2$ (105). Cf. *connected*.

Weakly linear frame (model): *Frame* (*model*) which is *reflexive*, *transitive* and *totally connected* (82). Cf. *linear*.

World: Member of W in a *frame* or *model* (7).

$\vdash_S \alpha$: α is a *theorem* of S.

$\dashv_S \alpha$: α is not a *theorem* of S.

$\Lambda \vdash_S \alpha$: see *deductive consequence*.

List of axioms for propositional systems

The formulae listed below are mentioned, on the pages indicated, as axioms for modal systems. All normal modal systems contain the elements mentioned on pp. 4f., viz. PC, **K**, US, MP, N, L-distribution, DR1, DR3, Eq and LMI.

The notation '$(=\alpha)$' after a formula means that adding that formula to the system K gives the same system as adding α to K.

1	**K**	$L(p \supset q) \supset (Lp \supset Lq)$	4
2	**T**	$Lp \supset p$	10
3	**4**	$Lp \supset LLp$	10
4	**B**	$\sim p \supset L \sim Lp$	10
5	**E**	$\sim Lp \supset L \sim Lp$	11
6		$p \supset LMp \, (= 4)$	15
7		$Mp \supset LMp \, (= 5)$	15
8	**D**	$Lp \supset Mp$	29
9	**D1**	$L(Lp \supset q) \vee L(Lq \supset p)$	30, 81
10	**G1**	$MLp \supset LMp$	31
11		Lp	34
12		$p \supset Lp$	35
13		$p \equiv Lp$	35
14		$L^n p$	36
15	**MV**	$MLp \vee Lp$	36, 57
16		$MLp \supset (p \supset Lp)$	38, 134
17		$Lp \supset LMLp$	38

18		$Mp \supset Lp$	39
19		$ML(p.\sim p) \vee L(p.\sim p)(=15)$	39
20		$MLp \vee Lq\,(=15)$	39
21	$\mathbf{W}_0$	$LM\top \supset L\bot\,(=15)$	39
22	$\mathbf{G}'$	$M^m L^n p \supset L^j M^k p$	42
23		$q \supset Lp\,(=11)$	46
24		$Mq \supset MLp\,(=15)$	46
25		$M(Lp.q) \supset L(Mq \vee p)(=9)$	46
26	$\mathbf{M}$	$LMp \supset MLp$	47
27		$MLp \supset Mp$	51
28		$MMLp \supset (Lp.Mp)$	51
29	$\mathbf{VB}$	$MLp \vee L(L(Lq \supset q) \supset q)$	57
30		$LMq \supset L(Lp \supset p)$	66
31		$L(L(Lp \supset p) \supset Lp)$	66
32		$L(p \equiv Lp) \supset Lp$	66
33		$L(Lp \supset p) \vee L(Lp \supset LLp)$	97
34	$\mathbf{W}$	$L(Lp \supset p) \supset Lp$	101, 146
35	$\mathbf{D1}_0$	$L(Lp.p) \supset q) \vee L((Lq.q) \supset p)$	105
36	$\mathbf{N1}$	$L(L(p \supset Lp) \supset p) \supset (MLp \supset p)$	107
37	$\mathbf{N1}'$	$L(\sim p \supset M(p.M\sim p)) \supset (MLp \supset p)\,(=36)$	107
38	$\mathbf{J1}$	$L(L(p \supset Lp) \supset p) \supset p$	111
39	$\mathbf{MV}'$	$LMp \supset Lq\,(=15)$	132
40		$Mp \equiv Lp$	133
41	$\mathbf{Mk}$	$(Lp.\sim LLp) \supset M(LLp.\sim LLLp)$	154
42	$\mathbf{Mk}'$	$L(LLp \supset LLLp) \supset (Lp \supset LLp)(=41)$	154
43	$\mathbf{Mk}^1$	$L(LLp \supset LLLq) \supset (Lq \supset LL(p \vee q))$	157
44	$\mathbf{Mk}^2$	$L(LLp \supset LLLq) \supset (Lp \supset LLq)$	157
45	$\mathbf{Mk}^3$	$L(LLp \supset Lq) \supset (Lp \supset q)$	157
46	$\mathbf{Mk}^{3'}$	$(Lp.q) \supset M(LLp.Mq)(=46)$	158

Index

Definitions of important terms will be found in the glossary on pp. 189–94.

197